Y0-CMP-650

Board of Directors

Jack W. Owen, Chairman
Bruce W. Sumner, Vice Chairman
Robert M. Coon, Jr., Secretary
Martha A. McSteen, President
Bette K. MacClelland
Thomas J. Marr, Jr.
Charles D. Baker
Winifred M. Hageman
M. David Paine, M.D.

To Protect and Improve Social Security... Make Every Voice Count.

The story behind one of the most effective grassroots organizations in America — dedicated to protecting and improving *your* Social Security and Medicare benefits.

**Edited and Compiled
by
David Deutsch**

To Protect and Improve Social Security...
Make Every Voice Count

The story behind one of the most effective grassroots organizations in the world — dedicated solely to protecting and improving your Social Security and Medicare benefits.

by
David Deutsch

Copyright ©1992
Dogwood Press

ALL RIGHTS RESERVED

Dedication

To the millions of members and supporters of the National Committee to Preserve Social Security and Medicare who, over the years, have contributed in so many ways to helping bring attention to senior issues.

Table of Contents

The National Committee to Preserve
Social Security and Medicare 1

    Questions and Answers
    about the National Committee 5

FACING THE ISSUES TOGETHER

Social Security...
A Favorite Target for Cutback 9

    Social Security Funding Debate Rages 9

    Stop Penalizing Hard-Working Seniors! 12

The Injustice of the Notch 16

    The Notch: A Thorn for Millions of Seniors 16

Medicare...an American Institution Under Siege 22

    Celebrating 25 Years of Medicare 22

    Medicare Cuts Squash Hospital Quality 25

    How to Use Medicare Wisely 27

    1992 Social Security and Medicare Figures 30

Reforming America's Health Care System 33

    The National Committee
    on Health Care Reform 33

    Looking for Answers to the
    National Health Care Crisis 35

    House Committee Looks
    at Health Reform 37

The Repeal of the Catastrophic Coverage Surtax 40
- The Catastrophic Coverage Fight 40
- What We Have Learned 42

Long-Term Care... A Long-Term Challenge 45
- The Need for Long-Term Care Insurance 45
- Buying Long-Term Care Insurance 48
- When Choosing a Nursing Home 49
- Family Members and Health Decisions 51

Ask Mary Jane 52

THE BEST OF "HEALTH TALK"

Eat and Exercise Your Way to Health 68
- Most Americans Lack Good Diet Knowledge 68
- Healthy Food Choices 70
- Controlling Your Cholesterol 71
- Exercise May Be Crucial for Senior Health 74

Drugs and Technology... Your Expanding Medical Options 77
- Prescription Drugs Handle With Care 77
- New Drug Therapies For Heart Attacks 79
- Influenza Vaccination an Annual Must 80
- Sleeping Pills May be Harmful 81

Ibuprofen Linked With Kidney Failure 81

Space Program Provides Medical Technology 82

Diseases of Special Concern to Seniors 85

Sleep Disorders 85

Incontinence...Avoidable and Treatable 87

Four Million With Alzheimer's Disease 88

Breast Cancer Screening Guidelines 89

Poor Vision and Hip Fracture 89

GETTING PERSONAL

National Committee Staff 92

Martha McSteen, President 92

Lloyd Duxbury 93

Martha Mohler 94

Monette McKinnon 96

Bente Cooney 97

Meet the Members 100

Edward Thomason 100

Nan Rogers 102

James W. Latimer, Jr. 103

Raymond and Ann Kolb 104

Leonard Fortner 106

Your Voice Helps Strengthen Social Security and Medicare? 108

Make Every Voice Count

Introduction

It's been said that the National Committee to Preserve Social Security and Medicare wrote the book on protecting the rights of seniors in this country.

Well, now here's a book about them!

Here is some of the best, most interesting, most useful information they've ever published, including articles from their popular newspaper, *Saving Social Security,* as well as reprints of some of their special booklets, brochures and news releases.

You'll find exciting descriptions of some of the challenges they've faced (and are still facing) to protect the interests of seniors, information on current issues of interest to seniors, valuable tips on what you can do to protect your Social Security and Medicare benefits, and plenty of facts about the latest medical advances affecting seniors.

Looking back over it all, I'm amazed at how much they've accomplished in just a few years.

And I'm almost overwhelmed by how much they still hope to accomplish to help make the Social Security and Medicare programs better for seniors, their children, and even their *grandchildren.*

So this is more than just a book to read and put on your bookshelf. It's an invitation! An invitation to learn more about the National Committee and join in their efforts to protect and improve two of our country's most important social programs.

David Deutsch
January, 1992

The National Committee to Preserve Social Security and Medicare

Founded in 1982, the National Committee is recognized as the most active and influential grassroots senior education and lobbying association in the U.S. Its mission: to protect and improve the Social Security and Medicare programs. It is totally independent from Congress, all government agencies and all political parties.

On August 14, 1935, the Social Security Act was signed, laying the cornerstone for the most successful social program in American history.

Thirty years later, on July 30, 1965, the Medicare program was established, adding health protection to income security for seniors. Seniors benefit from the Medicare program, which covers their basic medical expenses.

No other government programs are more essential to the security of American families.

But from time to time certain legislative and budgetary changes have been proposed that would weaken the programs and their benefits.

The National Committee to Preserve Social Security and Medicare was created to keep seniors apprised of these proposed changes. And to give them a collective voice — plus direct lobbying influence in the legislative process which has such a direct effect on their benefits.

Working to Build Better Benefits

Funded almost entirely by dues and contributions from millions of members and supporters, the National Committee works full-time to protect and improve Social Security and Medicare benefits and to educate its members and the public about these programs.

This significant contribution to such important federal programs by a private group is furthered by the three principles of the National Committee:

1. Education. The National Committee educates its members as well as the general public, the political community, and working professionals in health care and aging about specific issues that affect the quality of life for seniors in America.

2. Innovation. The National Committee employs some of America's more knowledgeable authorities on Social Security and Medicare. They monitor and respond to questions, suggestions, and complaints seniors have about Social Security and Medicare. Consequently, they are in a unique position to formulate and suggest innovations and practical improvements to Social Security and Medicare from the *beneficiary's* perspective.

3. Action. An important function of the National Committee is to lobby members of Congress to vote against any bills which might weaken these two programs — and to

vote for positive improvements in them. Through mailed *Legislative Alerts* and a regularly published newspaper, *Saving Social Security,* seniors in America are kept informed of proposed changes to Social Security and Medicare — and how these changes might affect these benefits.

The National Committee makes it a priority to listen to what its members have to say, through polls, surveys and focus groups, as well as through thousands of letters and telephone calls from members every month.

Not Affiliated with the Government

The National Committee is a non-profit organization with millions of members and supporters, mostly seniors, who have united for the protection and improvement of their rightful retirement benefits.

From modest membership dues (just $10 annually), plus voluntary donations, they staff their Washington office with some of the most experienced and professional experts on Social Security and Medicare in America today. Consequently, members receive the most up-to-the-minute information about these programs and the effects they will have upon seniors.

Vigilant Lobbyists Work Full Time for You

Led by Executive Vice-President Max Richtman (Harvard-educated, with almost 20 years on Capitol Hill), their job is crucial.

When proposals arise that may affect seniors unfavorably — or before bills concerning these benefits can be voted on — lobbyists are on the scene. Their presentation of the "senior side" of the issues — whether preparing position papers, persuading undecided members of Congress, or educating the uninformed — makes an important contribution to the democratic process.

In fact, these activities, guided by the opinions and wishes of the membership, have influenced legislation that otherwise might have been costly in terms of benefits that might have been adversely affected.

Influence Through Education and Member Action

The National Committee's influence in Washington stems from their ability to inform politicians and members and to rally members and supporters to immediate action on any issue involving their benefits.

Almost at a moment's notice, they can alert members — and trigger an avalanche of members' postcards, petitions, and telephone calls that inform politicians of what seniors believe is right. This fast and formidable response has helped defeat several unfavorable proposals — often, in the nick of time.

In 1990, when Congressional leaders and the White House tried to *double* the Medicare deductible and increase the monthly premium (the largest hike in its history), the National Committee, backed by a barrage of postcards from their members, played a major role in convincing Congress to reduce their proposal by over 60%.

In 1988, when a law was passed which taxed seniors up to an additional $1,600 per couple ($800 for singles) for "catastrophic coverage" under Medicare, the National Committee led the opposition to this unfair law. Congress was persuaded to repeal the law and abolish the tax.

In 1987, when the Administration tried to permanently reduce the Social Security cost-of-living adjustment (COLA) by 2%, the National Committee delivered over 8,000,000 signed petitions to Congress. The proposal was withdrawn.

The Most Important Moments Are Ahead

In addition to defending these programs, the National

Committee vigorously promotes much-needed improvements to them. They want to see every working American enjoy freedom from uncertainty and calamity.

Potential improvements include coverage of both long-term home health care and nursing home care, eliminating the earnings test, correction of the Notch, and other innovations.

Questions and Answers about the National Committee

From time to time, members and prospective members contact the National Committee with questions. These are some of the most frequently asked. This list is by no means comprehensive, so if you have a question not covered here, please feel free to write: The National Committee, 2000 K St., NW, Washington, DC 20006.

Q. What does it cost to be a member?

A. Annual dues are $10. Any contribution of $10 automatically makes you (and your spouse) a member of the National Committee. That is all you need pay.

However, membership dues alone do not support the many activities of the National Committee. So, from time to time, you may be asked to help finance projects of particular interest to you. Additional contributions are entirely voluntary.

Q. What do I get for my membership dues?

A. First and foremost, you get to be a part of one of the most effective grassroots education and advocacy efforts ever organized on behalf of seniors.

You are automatically enrolled in the National Committee's Legislative Alert Service, which means you will be notified promptly of fast-breaking developments in Washington. You'll learn just when a letter or phone call from you will carry the most weight with your Congressman or Senator.

In addition, you will receive eight copies a year of the membership newspaper, *Saving Social Security*, which is chock full of news on what Congress is doing for you — or to you.

"Senior Flash," the National Committee's telephone hotline at (202) 822-9187, will provide you with weekly updates of what's going on in the House and Senate.

The National Committee also publishes brochures on a wide range of subjects of interest to seniors.

Q. Are dues refundable?

A. The National Committee is a no-nonsense, aggressive education and lobbying organization, so members sometimes decide the National Committee is not their cup of tea. Whatever the reason, members who wish to leave the organization are given a prompt refund of their $10.

Q. Are contributions tax deductible?

A. Because of the National Committee's lobbying activities, dues and contributions are not deductible.

Q. Is there a way to get really involved in National Committee lobbying efforts?

A. The National Committee's grassroots department is always looking for individuals who want to get actively involved in lobbying for a specific legislative goal. If you want to organize activists at the local or state level, by all means let the grassroots department know. Call (202) 822-9459 or write the Washington office.

Q. How does the National Committee spend its money?

A. Education and legislative advocacy are the main functions of the National Committee. Consequently, over the last three fiscal years, about 58 cents of every dollar given to the National Committee — in dues or contributions — was spent educating members and the general public about problems facing seniors; educating seniors about specific programs created for their benefit; discussing legislative needs; lobbying in support of or in opposition to bills pending before Congress; and promoting new and innovative legislative and regulatory concepts.

In the past three years, fund-raising costs have taken an average of 16 percent of income, while administrative costs, on average, claimed another 20 percent. Administrative expenses in part reflect the high cost — in paper, printing and postage — of using the mail to communicate with members, potential members and the public. But since direct mail so effectively galvanizes individuals into action, the National Committee believes the cost is justified. An average of 6 percent of dues and contributions have gone into a reserve in the past three years.

Q. How can I get more information about the financial status of the National Committee?

A. A copy of the latest National Committee audited financial statement is available upon request. Also, the National Committee makes copies of its financial reports available to most state governments. Check with either the office of the attorney general or the Office of Consumer Affairs in your state.

FACING THE ISSUES TOGETHER

Today, many issues affect the quality of life for seniors: Social Security, Medicare, the Notch, health care reform and long-term care. In the following chapters, you'll see how these issues affect seniors, and how the National Committee works for legislation in the best interest of seniors. You'll also find some ways to protect your own — and your family's — health and financial security.

. . .

Social Security... A Favorite Target for Cutback

Social Security Funding Debate Rages

Want some insights into how the system really works? Read the story of Senator Moynihan's attempts in 1990 to reform Social Security funding.

Sen. Daniel Patrick Moynihan's, D-N.Y., controversial proposal to roll back the recent increase in the Social Security tax may have polarized legislators, but it is also forcing them to take a hard look at the whole issue of Social Security funding.

"This roll back gives a median income family in 1991 just under $400 a year," said Moynihan. "The people paying the tax need the money and the trust fund doesn't. It is their money, not general revenue."

In addition to repealing the 1990 increase, Moynihan's bill would roll back the 1991 rate from 6.2 percent to 5.1 percent over the next 20 years. After 2012, his plan calls for a gradual rise in the tax rate until 2045, when the rate will reach 8.1 percent.

National Committee President Martha McSteen, in testimony before the Senate Finance Committee, said Moynihan "has done the nation a favor by focusing national attention on the way the Social Security surplus is being used to disguise the true size of the budget deficit."

"Removing the trust funds from the budget calculations is essential to maintain the integrity of the Social Security system," she continued. "It's much like getting rid of the ice cream and doughnuts before you go on a diet — you remove the temptation and force yourself to make the tough decisions."

Mrs. McSteen told the Finance Committee that National Committee members support reduced payroll taxes so long as benefits are not reduced.

"Traditional pay-as-you-go financing provides a basis for stable financing of Social Security fair to both taxpayers and beneficiaries," she said.

However, there is plenty of opposition to the Moynihan plan. The late Sen. John Heinz, R-Penn., called it a "sugar coated poison pill," while Office of Management and Budget Director Richard Darman likens the proposal to "a grenade thrown in the middle of the House and Senate."

Social Security Administration Commissioner Gwendolyn King, reflecting the administration's view, called the proposal irresponsible. And the National Association of Manufacturers opposes the tax cut because of the likelihood corporate income taxes would be increased to replace lost revenue.

However, the bill is firmly supported by the Chamber of Commerce and the Heritage Foundation.

Still others, while agreeing in principle to a cut in Social Security taxes, have reservations about the exact provisions of the bill.

Moynihan insists Social Security benefits would not be threatened and contends that tax rates in the bill would fully finance benefits and maintain a safe reserve fund for 20 years longer than the current system. The reduction in the trust fund surplus would force lawmakers to deal with the true size of the national deficit, he says.

Social Security Administration statistics reveal that nearly three out of four taxpayers will pay more under FICA in 1990 (counting employers' matching contribution) than they pay in federal income tax. In the past decade, Social Security taxes rose 23 percent, shifting the burden of taxation from income tax to Social Security tax — from the wealthy to the middle class and poor.

"By what right and for how long do we continue to make the deficit the peculiar burden of people who get paid by the hour?" Moynihan remarked.

Whatever the outcome of this heated debate, Moynihan is satisfied that he accomplished an important objective — by introducing this legislation, he has exposed the misuse of the Social Security Trust Funds, and directed the nation's attention to the future of Social Security. 4/90

Stop Penalizing Hard-Working Seniors!

The National Committee believes it is grossly unfair that the Social Security earnings test penalizes senior citizens who wish to continue working. Believe it or not, the reason for this dates back to the Great Depression. In the following story, you'll also find out why you may be eligible for Social Security benefits for several months this year even if you continue to work at earnings substantially over the Social Security annual earnings limitation.

When most folks reach 65, they want to leave their jobs and retire. But many senior Americans — out of either personal preference or financial necessity — want to remain in the work force.

Unfortunately, they are often in for a shock.

Many seniors don't expect to live on Social Security alone. However, they don't expect to be financially penalized for working either. This penalty comes from an antiquated law still on the books which has its roots in the Great Depression. It was designed to get those age 65 and older out of the work force to make room for the younger generation. While times have changed, this law hasn't.

Take, for example, the case of Eloise B., a 66-year-old widow from upstate New York who must work to supplement her modest Social Security benefits to pay her rent, utilities, food and health insurance bills. Yet, because she earned more than $9,360 last year, part of her Social Security benefits were taken away from her.

Is this fair? Hardly.

The earnings limit is indexed automatically to the average wage increase and is sure to go up again this year. In

1991 seniors between 65 and 69 who continued to work lost $1 in benefits for every $3 they earned in excess of $9,720. But unearned income — such as dividends and other investments — which can be substantial for upper income individuals, is not affected by the earnings test at all.

Faced with continued double-digit increases in health costs, senior Americans with even moderate incomes are trapped in a Catch-22 situation. If they continue to work they may lose Social Security benefits. Without the extra income, they often face living near poverty.

The truth is the Social Security earnings test hits hardest those least able to afford it.

It is pure folly to pursue a policy that shuts out people who want to work and contribute on the economic sidelines. When it was crafted half a century ago, the earnings test was meant to open up scarce jobs for young workers with families to support. Today's business climate is vastly different from the Depression.

It's high time we put an end to an outdated policy that creates such economic and social harm. All Americans, regardless of age, should have the freedom to work without fear of being penalized and losing hard-earned benefits.

Working Seniors: Don't Miss Your Benefits

You may be eligible for Social Security benefits for several months this year even if you continue to work at earnings *well over the Social Security annual earnings limitation. The same is true for dependent spouses and widow(er)s of retired workers.*

Social Security *tests* whether an applicant for benefits has actually retired by looking at current earnings. If an insured worker, dependent spouse, or widow(er) has little or no earnings, Social Security benefits are payable every month of the year. In 1991, eligible individuals aged 65 through 69 were considered fully retired — and eligible for 12 months of benefits — if annual earnings did not exceed $9,720.

But some benefits might be payable even if earnings are considerably over this exempt amount. Over $9,720, $1 in benefits is offset for every $3 in excess earnings — much better than the $1 for $2 offset which formerly applied.

Social Security can tell you if you are eligible for some benefits or you can quite easily determine the answer yourself. Here's how:

Call Social Security at 1-800-234-5772 and ask how much you are eligible to receive in monthly Social Security benefits. Multiply your monthly benefits by 12 to learn how much you could receive in Social Security benefits this year.

Then estimate your 1991 earnings. From your earnings, subtract the $9,720 exempt amount to determine the excess. Divide your excess earnings by three (because the offset is only one-third) and subtract the answer from your full year's Social Security benefits. The difference is the benefits you are eligible to receive this year even if you do not "retire."

Individuals under age 65 have a lower exempt amount — $7,080 in 1991 — and are still subject to a $1 offset for each $2 of excess earnings.

Beginning with the month any worker reaches age 70, there is no longer an earnings test. Full benefits are paid every month without regard to earnings.

Make Every Voice Count

The Injustice of the Notch

The Notch is a glitch in the retirement benefits structure that means some 12 million Americans — half of all retired workers — receive checks from 10 to 20 percent smaller than those born immediately before or after them. Yet the Commissioner of Social Security claims the Notch doesn't even exist! Read these articles and decide for yourself.

The Notch: A Thorn for Millions of Seniors

The Notch — the result of Congressional action taken in 1977 to correct an earlier legislative misjudgment — is one of the most blatant inequities in the Social Security system.

The Notch affects nearly 12 million Americans born between 1917 and 1926 — half of all retired workers — causing seniors in this bracket to receive benefit checks smaller than those born a few years earlier or a few years later. (This also hurts the retired worker's family, since spouse and dependent benefits are based on the worker's benefits. The same holds for survivor benefits.)

There is no logical explanation why two people with similar work histories should have vastly different monthly Social Security benefits. But this is exactly what the government has allowed to occur.

A Tale of Two Sisters

To illustrate this problem, look at two sisters born one year apart, one in 1916 and the other in 1917, and retired after 25 years.

They worked for the same company doing the same job for the same pay. During their careers, they paid virtually the same in Social Security taxes.

But this is where the similarity ends. When it came time to receive their Social Security benefits, the sister born in 1917 drew 20.9 percent less.

And despite our long political tradition of correcting inequities, there has been no real acceptance of the need to address the Notch issue in Congress. So distrust of the government exists among many senior Americans today.

We now have the opportunity to eliminate this distrust. So far, more than 60% of the House of Representatives and 40% of the Senate have recognized this inequity and endorsed legislation to correct it. And the number of co-sponsors surely will have risen by the time you read this.

An Affordable Solution

National Committee staff and seniors on our National Notch Advisory Council have worked with Congressional advocates in both the House and Senate to unite behind a consensus bill to correct the Notch.

This legislation has received overwhelming bipartisan support — since correction of the Notch poses no threat to our Social Security system. Even after correcting the Notch, the annual Social Security Trust Funds reserve would grow by over $100 billion a year during the 1990s.

Many seniors are victims of the Notch. And it has understandably caused a lot of bitterness and resentment during a time which is supposed to be the golden part of their lives. This is precisely why the National Committee continues to remain in the forefront of the fight to correct this inequity.

The effort to correct the Notch has been an uphill battle from the very beginning, and many obstacles still must be overcome. Some House and Senate leaders — people who can influence whether or not the legislation actually moves — have not been supportive of legislative Notch reform efforts.

It is not easy to get a bill passed today. In fact, while several thousand bills might be introduced during the two years of a Congress, only a handful actually will become law.

The Notch on Capitol Hill

The Notch bill was referred to the Ways and Means Committee in the House and the Finance Committee in the Senate.

Unfortunately, only six of the 20 senators on the Finance Committee and only 10 of 35 members of the Ways and Means Committee had co-sponsored the consensus Notch legislation at this writing. Unless we can get majorities on both these committees, the normal legislative process will be stymied.

But our Congressional allies are preparing several legislative tactics to get the bill out of committee. It is unfortunate, but such extraordinary procedures may be the only way to spur the Ways and Means Committee to action.

On the bright side, we have Congressional support for the Notch bill in all but five states — Delaware, Idaho, Vermont, Maine and Wyoming. In several states the bill is supported by the entire Congressional delegation.

If your delegation is not solidly behind the bill, please let your members of Congress know how you feel. They need your input.

Simply put, the government cannot expect to enjoy

credibility as the guardian of the people's interests if it continues to permit a disparity such as the Notch to exist.
11/91

Notch Victims, Undaunted, Press On

"Notch victims are restless and they're angry. They feel Congress is stalling and they don't like it. They want action now."

So reports National Committee Legislative Affairs Director Lloyd Duxbury after taking part in a series of fall Notch meetings from Indiana to New York. Duxbury was out taking the pulse of older Americans on the Notch issue and the consensus is clear — Notch victims are tired of waiting for Congress to address their concerns.

Notch defenders in Washington clearly are feeling the heat from victims across the country and, as a result, are scrambling for ways to stem the growing tide of resentment — resentment sure to be felt at the polls in November, say Notch experts.

Social Security Commissioner Gwendolyn King, worried about growing support to abolish the Notch in Congress, sent a position paper to lawmakers which said the Notch doesn't exist and therefore shouldn't be fixed.

"Although some people sincerely believe an injustice has been done, the truth is that they are being treated fairly and getting the benefits that Congress intended," her paper says.

"The cost of pending Notch correction legislation could be extremely high — one bill would cost up to $860 billion over 10 years," the paper contends.

However, Congressional experts concluded the current consensus Notch bill — the one which a majority in Congress supports — would cost only $4.6 billion per year over 10 years, a small fraction of the current trust fund surplus.

To further counteract the work of Notch activists, House Ways and Means Committee Chairman Dan Rostenkowski, D-Ill., and Ranking Minority Member Bill Archer, R-Texas, have written to their colleagues describing ways to deflect Notch questions from constituents.

Adding further pressure was a letter to lawmakers from the Leadership Council of Aging Organizations, whose members include organizations such as the American Association of Retired Persons, the National Council of Senior Citizens and the Gray Panthers.

Even the White House is voicing opposition to Notch legislation. National Committee member Martha Parnell recently wrote the President asking his support for the cause. Special Assistant to the President Shirley Green responded by saying, "The President has promised to oppose any measure that would 'mess around' with Social Security benefits and that would threaten the integrity of the Social Security Trust Funds."

However, Bush had previously voiced support for Notch correction in an article written in the August 1988 *Saving Social Security*.

"I am concerned about the Notch inequality," he wrote then. "People should not get different benefit levels just because they happen to be born in one year instead of another."

The drive to dissuade Members of Congress from supporting Notch legislation appears to be backfiring. It merely has caused activists to redouble efforts to force a vote on the issue.

In meetings, rallies and forums across the nation, word of the Notch injustice is spreading quickly. Petition deliveries, such as one in Rhode Island, where over 4,000 signatures were presented to Rep. Jack Reed, D-R.I., let Congress know these voters mean business.

All We Want is a Vote

"The most important thing any Notch family can do is contact their lawmakers to push for an up or down floor vote on this issue," says Duxbury, the National Committee's Legislative Affairs Director. "This is all we're asking for — a chance for the issue to be decided once and for all."

With a record number of co-sponsors signed on to Notch legislation — 270 in the House and 42 in the Senate — Notch victims should be asking their legislators why a vote has not been taken to date, Duxbury continued.

National Committee President Martha McSteen, Executive Vice President Max Richtman, Deputy PAC Director Susan Dahlquist and Notch expert Allen Johnston continue to meet with Congressmen and Senators to persuade them of the bill's merits.

"We are trying to convince legislators that fixing the Notch is not only fair for millions of beneficiaries, but it also makes good economic sense," says Richtman. "After all, dollars given back to Notch victims will eventually be pumped back into our sluggish economy." 12/91

Medicare... an American Institution Under Siege

Although Medicare serves more than 33 million seniors and disabled annually, it has been undergoing changes and modifications for many of its 25 years. In this chapter, you'll hear from a Medicare insider on how Medicare was born and evolved, and find out how the National Committee opposes Medicare cutbacks. You'll also find a valuable guide to the ins and outs of the Medicare system.

Celebrating 25 Years of Medicare

Martha McSteen, President of the National Committee, was one of the ten original Regional Medicare Administrators. In this article, she offers her insights into this unique American institution to commemorate Medicare's 25th anniversary in 1990.

Twenty-five years ago we embarked on a grand adventure. Before 1965, many moderate and low income seniors went without health care because they could not afford it.

Make Every Voice Count

Our solution was Medicare, the federal government's first foray into health care. Originally proposed during the Truman administration, the idea was to deliver quality hospital and health care to older Americans — regardless of income.

The Health Insurance for the Aged Act was signed July 30, 1965, by President Lyndon B. Johnson at the Truman Library in Independence, Mo. One year later, Medicare began. While the program has had its share of problems, we all can agree it — along with Social Security — is vital to an improved quality of life for older Americans and their families.

At the beginning we felt a mixture of joy and consternation. A giant of untold dimensions in health care was appearing on the American scene. And at last, health care was formally recognized as a right — just as education always had been perceived as a right. This was a crucial turning point for senior Americans.

Only one year lapsed between the signing of the Medicare Act and the start of the new program — what a challenge! It was an incredibly short time to create an enormous health care system and build unheard of partnerships in the health care field.

We had just one year to develop Medicare — scores of regulations to write and terms to define to create an organization to ultimately serve more than 33 million seniors and disabled annually. It meant all of us involved had to work quickly and be extremely creative. A special challenge was ensuring that all seniors had full access to the program, regardless of race, creed or religion.

A Unique Partnership

All the traditional players in the health care field were brought together with the federal government to create Medicare — the American Medical Association;

the American Hospital Association; the Nursing Home Association; the Home Health agencies; Blue Cross/Blue Shield; private health insurers such as Aetna, Mutual of Omaha and Equitable; public health administrations and state departments of health.

Medicare marked the first time the government was seen as a key player in the health care field. This deeply concerned the other, fiercely independent players. Credit is properly given to the private sector and state governments for their willingness to extend a hand to the federal government and make Medicare a viable system.

Negotiations were indeed quite difficult — and many of the parties were quite apprehensive about the new program. There were intense moments when the members of this new partnership seemed deadlocked on an issue. But perseverance and open dialogue brought about an amicable solution most of the time.

Medicare was very fortunate that many of the strongest, most highly motivated, most experienced leaders within the Social Security Administration were tapped for the mammoth process of building one of the world's largest health care systems.

Being one of the original 10 regional Medicare administrators was the pinnacle of my career in the federal government — even more exciting and challenging than my tenure as acting Social Security commissioner. We had the opportunity to give shape to something which would eventually become part of nearly everyone's life.

Medicare has a great history of service — and not just to senior citizens. Soon after its creation, experts called for adding others in need of health coverage — hundreds of thousands receiving disability benefits from Social Security and the railroad retirement system, plus those whose work years ended before they could qualify for Social Security.

In 1967 President Johnson proposed bringing them under Medicare. Congress did so in 1972.

Of course, Medicare has gone through many changes over the years, especially in the area of cost control. In 1983, prospective payment was introduced as a way to hold down the skyrocketing costs experienced by hospitals.

Update for the '90s Needed

On its 25th anniversary, Medicare does a herculean job providing health care to America's seniors and disabled. We've come a long way since 1965, yet I believe Medicare needs an update for the '90s.

I'd like to see Medicare provide a base to build comprehensive long-term care to all Americans — a long-term care plan where the public sector takes the lead, yet the private sector plays a strong role. I feel this is a totally appropriate role for Medicare.

The challenge today is to ensure quality, accessible and cost-effective care for today's seniors as well as tomorrow's.
7/90

Medicare Cuts Squash Hospital Quality

This next article will give you some insight into what is, unfortunately, becoming an annual event — fighting the administration's attempts to reduce Medicare spending. The National Committee and other opponents of such cuts won this victory in 1991. They'll probably need all the help they can get in 1992!

Hospitals' ability to adequately serve their communities

will be severely impaired if the draconian budget cuts proposed by the Bush administration are actually enacted, senior advocates and hospital officials warn.

In his fiscal 1992 budget, President Bush wants to reduce Medicare spending by another $25 billion over the next five years. Senior advocates see this as a breach of last year's budget agreement, which saw Medicare cuts of $44 billion over five years.

Hospitals are asked to absorb 66 percent, or $16.5 billion, of this cut. One major area of Medicare cuts would be payments made to teaching hospitals — about $8.8 billion, cuts which the National Committee feels might result in a shortage of primary care doctors or specialists.

"We are extremely concerned about the long-term implications of these budget driven proposals on access and quality of care," National Committee President Martha McSteen said in written testimony to the House Ways and Means Health Subcommittee.

Hospitals Already Lose Money on Medicare

"In recent years, federal government reimbursement policies have made it impossibly difficult for health care professionals and their institutions to provide needed Medicare services to seniors, the disabled and the poor," says Mrs. McSteen.

The remaining $7.7 billion in proposed cuts likely would worsen the financial difficulties hospitals experience as the population ages, American Hospital Association Executive Vice President Paul Rettig says. "Hospitals continue to lose money on Medicare patients."

Rural hospitals may be the hardest hit by the administration's proposed cuts. Although rural hospitals try to maintain quality care, they struggle with high operating costs and staff shortages.

Medicare patients usually comprise about 70 to 80 percent of rural hospitals' patients. "And when those types [of] hospitals continue to lose money treating Medicare patients, it is only a matter of time until they will fail," Rep. Byron L. Dorgan, D-N.D., told the subcommittee.

Observers believe the Bush budget proposal will not get past either house of Congress. "Medicare cuts of the size we're hearing about would put severe strains on the ability of hospitals to cover rising medical costs," says Senate Finance Committee Chairman Lloyd Bentsen, Texas. "It is simply unacceptable." 5/91 [Editor's Note: Fortunately, this time, it *was* unacceptable.]

How to Use Medicare Wisely

Know When to Sign Up

Seniors new to Medicare need to be aware of a new six-month grace period in which medigap insurance cannot be denied due to medical condition. Also, if you didn't enroll when first eligible for Medicare, you need to know about the open enrollment period.

For the first time, enrollees age 65 and older can take advantage of a new federal law which says for the first six months after Medicare Part B coverage begins, insurance companies cannot deny a senior a medigap policy for health reasons. And, once in effect, medigap coverage cannot be taken away for health reasons.

Before the new law went into effect, medigap insurers often rejected seniors with health conditions such as heart disease or a disability.

Insurance companies still can impose a six-month waiting period before a policy holder can receive coverage for a pre-existing condition, but he or she cannot be denied coverage because of that condition.

Many insurance companies are worried about the adverse consequences of these provisions, and may not tell consumers about their enrollment rights.

For seniors who did not sign up for Medicare Part B coverage when first eligible, the annual open enrollment period — Jan. 1 to March 31, 1992 — offers an opportunity to obtain this valuable protection.

It is important to sign up for benefits promptly because there is no limit to the number of years for which the penalty can be assessed, National Committee experts warn.

Monthly premiums — $31.80 in 1992 — are increased 10 percent each full year enrollment is delayed. Medicare originally imposed this penalty to ensure people did not wait until their health declined to join the program.

No penalty is imposed if you delay Medicare coverage because you have health insurance from a current employer or a spouse's current employer.

Also, seniors age 65 and older who are not eligible for Social Security or railroad retirement benefits may buy into the Medicare Part A program. In 1992, persons who enter the program in this way must pay a premium of $192 per month to finance their hospital care.

Help with Out-of-Pocket Costs

If your income and savings are below the poverty level, you can get help from Medicaid to pay those out-of-pocket costs.

Your state is now required to pay your Medicare premiums, deductibles and co-payments if you are eligible for Medicare and have an income below the federal poverty guideline of $6,620; $8,880 for couples. (A few states use different guidelines.)

It's called the Qualified Medicare Beneficiary program, or simply QMB.

To qualify, you must meet not only the income guidelines, but also the assets guidelines. The asset limit for the QMB program this year is $4,000 for an individual and $6,000 for couples.

The house you live in is not counted as an asset. States determine eligibility, so to find out if you qualify for this important benefit, contact your state or local agency that administers the Medicaid program, such as the Social Services Department or Health Department.

Seniors usually need purchase only Part B Medical Insurance. But, those individuals over age 65 not eligible for Social Security cash benefits can buy Medicare hospital insurance by paying Part A premiums of $192 each month.

So, if you qualify for the QMB program, both Part A and Part B premiums and all deductibles and co-payments will be paid by Medicaid. In addition, doctors and other health care providers are required to accept assignment (charge no more than Medicare allows) when caring for QMB-eligible individuals. This means there will be no cost to you.

In future years, people with incomes up to 110% (and later 120%) of poverty can be helped with Medicare premiums only.

Watching Medical Costs

Good news: New rules just issued affecting Medicare payments will help cut excessive and unnecessary medical charges.

Should your doctor schedule you for a medical test four or five days before your hospital admission, ask if the test could be delayed a day or two.

If your medical tests are done within three days of your hospital admission, their cost is incorporated into your hospital bill. Medicare will cover them, saving you the cost of the tests — or at least those tests approved by Medicare.

Medicare's intermediaries have been instructed not to reimburse any diagnostic services furnished to hospital inpatients within three days before the patients' admission, because Medicare considers these services included in the cost of hospitalization. This is true regardless of whether the services are related to admission.

Here's how it all works. Diagnostic and other services prior to a hospital admission provided on the day of admission, and for three days prior, will be included in the Part A hospital reimbursement. It therefore will be a savings for beneficiaries who will no longer have to pay for any of this under Part B. The new law basically extends the existing 24-hour rule to 72 hours. It is an effort to prevent "unbundling" of services. Coverage was effective January 1, 1991, for all diagnostic services, and as of October 1, 1991, the three-day limit also includes "any other services" such as physical therapy, chemotherapy and tumor radiation prior to an operation.

1992 Social Security and Medicare Figures

Social Security

Social Security cost-of-living adjustment	3.7%
Maximum benefit for worker retiring at 65 in 1992	$1,088
Average benefit for retired worker	$629
Maximum earnings subject to Soc. Sec. tax	$55,500
Earnings exempt from retirement test, under 65	$7,440/yr
Earnings exempt from retirement test, 65-69	$10,200/yr

Supplemental Security Income

Maximum allowable assets for individuals	$2,000
Maximum allowable assets for couples	$3,000
Maximum benefit for individuals	$422/mo
Maximum benefit for couples	$633/mo

Medicare

Supplemental Medical Insurance (Part B) premium	$31.80/mo
Part A deductible for 1st 60 days of illness	$652
Co-payment for days 61-90	$163/day
Co-payment for lifetime reserve days	$326/day
Co-payment for days 21-100 of skilled nursing care	$81.50/day
Hospital Insurance (Part A) buy-in premium*	$192/mo
Max. earnings subject to Medicare tax	$130,200/yr

Qualified Medicare Beneficiary Program**

Maximum allowable assets for individuals	$4,000
Maximum allowable assets for couples	$6,000
Maximum income for individuals to receive benefit	$6,620/yr**
Maximum income for couples to receive benefit	$8,880/yr**

* All individuals eligible for Social Security or railroad retirement benefits are automatically covered and do not pay Part A premiums. Only those who do not qualify at age 65 for Social Security or railroad retirement benefits must pay the Part A premium if they want Medicare coverage.

** Maximum income figures for the QMB program will be readjusted around April 1992. The new income figures then will be retroactive to January 1992.

Make Every Voice Count

By permission—Ramirez and Copley News Service

Reforming America's Health Care System

Most Americans today, whether seniors or not, agree that America's health care system is badly in need of reform. The National Committee is deeply concerned about the quality and affordability of health care. In this important chapter, you'll discover some surprising facts about health care today, and learn how the National Committee is working to make health care more accessible and affordable.

The National Committee on Health Care Reform

Almost 34 million people, or close to 14% of Americans, go without health care protection at any given time. When looked at over time, many more people are vulnerable. For example, during a recent 28-month period, 63 million people lacked any health insurance during all or part of that time. Few Americans are protected against the catastrophic costs of long-term care.

In 1980, little more than ten years ago, we spent $230 billion on health care. Last year, we spent $671 billion, or close to two billion dollars a day. Health care expenditures constitute an ever greater percent of our GNP. Currently, health care costs take up 12.2 percent of the GNP — up from 11.8 percent in 1989.

The National Committee is deeply concerned about health care spending and the fact that many hard working people go without adequate health care protection. Many of these people are the children and grandchildren of National Committee members.

In efforts to alleviate these problems, numerous bills with very different approaches have been introduced in Congress. As health care bills are introduced, the National Committee will continue to keep its membership informed and always look forward to members' reactions and observations. When there is sufficient information about the various bills, the National Committee will survey its members asking for their opinions and comments.

From previous surveys and meetings with its membership, the National Committee recognizes that there are certain principles that must be included in a bill. These are some of the areas of concern:

- Access to health care for 100% of the population.
- Access to long-term care in the home, the community and the nursing home for all ages.
- Quality of care must be maintained and strengthened.
- Health care costs must be brought under control while maintaining and improving access to care.
- Financing of any universal and long-term care health care system must be by a broad-based social insurance program. 10/91

Looking for Answers to the National Health Care Crisis

This article is by Harvey I. Sloane, M.D., a consultant to the National Committee for health care reform. A graduate of Yale University and Case Western Reserve Medical School, Sloane spent several years as director of a Louisville, Ky. neighborhood clinic. He became Louisville's mayor and, in 1990, was the Democratic nominee for the U.S. Senate from Kentucky. Dr. Sloane frequently addresses health care reform issues in Saving Social Security.

National health care has been an issue in American politics throughout much of this century.

Teddy Roosevelt called for universal health care for all Americans while campaigning for the presidency under the Bull Moose Party banner. And the American Medical Association supported the call.

Three decades later, another President Roosevelt — Franklin, this time — wanted to make national health care a part of the Social Security program introduced in 1935, but didn't.

Four years later, the first legislative national health care package, the Wagner-Dingell bill, was introduced.

In 1948, President Truman made the call for national health care a part of his election campaign.

President Richard Nixon sent a universal health insurance proposal to Congress in 1971.

And every Congress since 1970 has seen Sen. Ted Kennedy, D-Mass., introduce a universal health care bill.

Why has national health care reform now become a dominant issue in the 1990s when, despite the support shown throughout this century, no really significant action has been taken? The issue is economics.

People are afraid to change jobs because they might lose

their health benefits. Families with a chronically ill child can find themselves unable to get health insurance coverage at all. Or, if they can obtain coverage, it will be through a policy with premiums which easily could increase 40 percent a year.

Even a well-off family can be wiped out financially just because one family member develops a catastrophic illness.

So the issue is no longer just health insurance for the unemployed and under-employed. The issue is affordable health care protection which can be provided without demolishing a family's finances.

The cost of medical care is the greatest reason why individuals file for personal bankruptcy today. Businesses — small and large — are affected deeply by skyrocketing prices. Workers are losing benefits, while businesses complain that the cost of providing health care to employees and retirees costs them a competitive edge in international trade.

Will this great problem be addressed? Chances are it will. The politicians in Washington are hearing from the folks back home. And there is some action.

Senate Majority Leader George Mitchell, D-Maine, has introduced a Democratic initiative. Another 10 to 15 health care proposals have been introduced in the House and Senate already — or soon will be.

Only the White House remains mute so far. But President George Bush says there will be an administration plan within 18 months.

If Bush were to lead the movement for affordable national health care, it could be for him what the restoration of relations with Red China was for President Nixon — a successful, surprising maneuver worthy of special mention in the history books.

It's going to take a national campaign to bring universal health care. All great social initiatives, from Social Security to Medicare to civil rights, require a national campaign.

But the national effort has begun already. And it will become more pronounced during the presidential campaign of 1992. By 1993 or 1994, we could see reform of a national health care system in a manner which gives everyone health insurance coverage and which controls costs.

We certainly will see it happen in this decade.

But that won't signal the end of the struggle. Universal health care is vital, but it doesn't solve the problems with long-term care for seniors and for disabled Americans. 8/91

House Committee Looks at Health Reform

In an unusual set of hearings this fall, the powerful House Ways and Means Committee took a comprehensive look at the plethora of bills introduced to reform the American health care delivery system.

Ninety-nine groups came before the committee to testify. The federal government, labor, business, medicine, science, consumer, insurance groups and others were given an opportunity to express their views on health care reform.

More than 30 different reform bills have been introduced in Congress. Generally, they take one of three approaches to solving the national health care dilemma:

- Pay or play. These plans would require businesses to provide health insurance coverage to all employees, or contribute a percentage of total payroll funds to finance a public insurance program.
- Single payer. Similar to the Canadian system, these plans would replace our current employer-based health insurance system with a government-run program to provide health care for all.
- Piecemeal approach. Generally favored by Republicans, these bills would use tax incentives, cost

controls and malpractice insurance reform to bring runaway health care spending into line.

National Committee President Martha McSteen also appeared before the panel. Although she withheld National Committee support from any one particular bill or plan, she let Congress know what provisions a health reform plan must include, stressing the need for long-term care protection.

"The National Committee supports the goal of affordable protection against the cost of acute and long-term care," she testified. "Any system must be a fair, public/private plan with cost containment and quality assurance measures."

Mrs. McSteen named several features National Committee members wish to see in any solution to the national health care crisis:

- Extension of Medicare benefits to those seniors over 65, mostly minorities, who do not qualify for coverage, and availability of public coverage for the uninsured.
- Coverage for preventive care services to help keep seniors healthy.
- Expansion of "transitional care" services, such as home health care, for those seniors whose illness isn't severe enough for hospital or nursing home stays. Elimination of the required three-day hospital stay necessary for Medicare to cover skilled nursing home care also would significantly improve transitional care and save money.

"National Committee members want protection from the high cost of long-term care," Mrs. McSteen said. "They also want to ensure their children and grandchildren have access to quality care. We wish to see the entire American family covered in a comprehensive way." 12/91

Make Every Voice Count

Reprinted By Permission of S. Kelly

The Repeal of the Catastrophic Coverage Surtax

One of the proudest accomplishments of the National Committee was its role in the repeal of the catastrophic surtax in 1989. It was truly an example of grassroots power at work. Here's the story behind that 33-month uphill battle, and some comments from Martha McSteen, President of the National Committee, on the lessons learned.

The Catastrophic Coverage Fight

For National Committee members, the House and Senate repeal of the catastrophic coverage surtax marked the culmination of a 33-month battle.

The effort began in early 1987, when Congress first looked at the proposal drafted by then Health and Human Services Secretary Otis Bowen. It was obvious that his suggestion didn't go far enough, so the National Committee gave its wholehearted endorsement to a bill introduced by the late Rep. Claude Pepper which would have provided real catastrophic coverage. That support was outlined in testimony after testimony presented to Congress.

Legislative alerts resulted in more than 100,000 handwritten letters and 220,000 petitions supporting the Pepper initiative. But once it became apparent H.R. 65 could not carry the day, the Florida Congressman introduced a long-term home health care bill, H.R. 2762. This too, quickly won the backing of the National Committee.

The House, however, ignored the letters and petitions and adopted legislation similar to what was finally enacted — a benefit package paid for entirely by seniors but which does not include long-term care.

As a result, a third legislative alert was sent to members, resulting in 120,000 letters to Senators, asking them to "support real catastrophic coverage legislation." Other efforts to inform senators and the American people of the weaknesses in the House bill included an article written by National Committee President Martha McSteen, which was sent to more than 2,500 newspapers across the nation, and an ad in *The Washington Post*.

The Senate, however, ignored seniors' pleas and followed the House in adopting legislation with "seniors-only" financing and no long-term care.

As conferees met to work out the differences in the House and Senate bills, they were greeted by ads in Washington newspapers, warning that "Seniors Won't Thank You," an article in *USA Today*, and more than 340,000 handwritten letters mailed as a result of a legislative alert urging Congress to "stop" the catastrophic coverage proposal and "go" with Pepper's home health care bill.

For a third time, the pleas of seniors were ignored and the final version of the Medicare Catastrophic Coverage Act — with "seniors-only" financing and no long-term care — was adopted by the conferees, approved by House and Senate and signed into law in July 1988, by then President Reagan.

At that time, many thought the battle was over. After all, they said, Congress seldom, if ever, revisits a law just months after its enactment.

But the more seniors learned about what the Medicare Catastrophic Coverage Act contained, the more upset they became.

The Battle Begins!

So, when the National Committee opened 1989 with a legislative alert urging members to send hand-written post cards to Congress to demand it revisit the issue, more than 1,200,000 pieces of mail flooded the Capitol. This was followed shortly by another 1,500,000 handwritten cards, supporting a broad-based alternative to the surtax, and by testimony from Mrs. McSteen.

National Committee lobbyists also worked the halls and committee rooms on both sides of the Capitol, urging members to heed their constituents.

"We've succeeded in correcting the flaws of the legislation passed last year," said Mrs. McSteen, "but the battle is far from over. It won't be over until Congress adopts some form of coverage for long-term health care, both in nursing homes and at home." 12/89

What We Have Learned

The author, Martha McSteen, is President of the National Committee.

During the time I spent working on the Medicare Catastrophic Coverage Act, I asked myself several times what we should learn from the rapid passage and repeal of what was called by some the greatest expansion of Medicare benefits since the program's inception.

The first, and perhaps the most important lesson, is that the political system works. You *can* fight City Hall — and win! That's a wonderful lesson for all Americans. Congress does listen to constituents, especially when they speak with one loud voice. And Congress is willing to acknowledge its mistakes and take steps to correct them.

A second lesson to be learned about the system: It is better to go a little slower and do a better job. Surely if Congress had not moved so swiftly, the members would have realized the weakness of the financing mechanism, especially of a large income surtax aimed at a small segment of the population.

The third lesson should be taken as a reminder. Our taxes, for the most part, come from everyone and are used for everyone. The reason everyone contributes to the cost of public education is that everyone benefits from having an educated populace. Everyone contributes to veterans' benefits because everyone has benefitted from the service veterans have provided. And everyone should contribute to health care costs because we all benefit, either directly or indirectly.

If a family member is ill, no matter the age of the individual, family resources are tapped. Helping older people maintain their financial independence, even in the face of severe illness, frees the resources of the entire family — and society in general — for other uses. Asking one segment of the population to pay for an entire program sets a bad precedent and violates an essential premise of our society, that we work together for the common good.

A fourth lesson is that Medicare does not cover long-term care costs. It did not do so before the catastrophic coverage expansion and it did not do so afterward. The so-called "historic" expansion of Medicare simply did not address the real need of our aging population: How to pay for extensive long-term care.

The debate surrounding the new legislation finally made

Americans aware that they do not have this crucial coverage. Previously, the public assumed that in the terrible event a family member needed nursing home care, Medicare would play some part in meeting the costs of that care. Now, a great many people realize this is not the case and are calling on Congress to enact a program to provide for both long-term home care and nursing home care.

The fifth lesson, one that we at the National Committee, particularly, have learned, is that being right does not necessarily make you popular. We told members of Congress early in the debate there were two major problems with the legislation they were considering — that the financing was unfair and not in keeping with social insurance principles, and that it lacked any significant provision for long-term care.

Now we stand accused by some members of Congress of inflaming seniors. The truth is that many senior citizens already were incensed by the flawed new law — now since repealed — and needed no encouragement. The more they learned about the program, the more opposed they became.

So, when I reflect on what I've learned, I can honestly answer, "I learned a lot. We all did." Seniors and members of Congress learned the right questions to ask the next time. Armed with these lessons, seniors now expect Congress to do nothing less than is decent, right and doable — finally to put America's long-term care crisis to bed. 1/89

Long-Term Care...
A Long-Term Challenge

Proper planning for the long-term care of yourself or someone you love may be one of the most important things you'll ever do. Unfortunately, anything connected with long-term care can be frustrating and confusing. The National Committee is working hard to change this — through education, as well as by actively working for better long-term care legislation.

The Need for Long-Term Care Insurance

Imagine purchasing a long-term care insurance policy, only later to find out you are not covered when a catastrophic illness forces you into a nursing home. As devastating as it may sound, this scenario happens far too often.

Seniors often are frustrated and confused over exactly

what long-term care policies cover and under what circumstances they will apply. As one National Committee member put it, "You need a law degree to understand these policies. They hide behind little, hard-to-read clauses."

Some Real Examples

Two 82-year-old National Committee members from Pompano Beach, Fla., purchased a long-term care policy several years ago — before the husband was diagnosed with Alzheimer's disease.

But when the wife, who had been caring for her husband since 1989, tried to place him in a nursing home, she discovered the long-term care policy for which she paid $1,500 annually would not cover her husband's nursing home care without a prior stay in the hospital.

In another case, a Chapel Hill, N.C. member who is 73 and suffers from severe angina, is deeply concerned about his future. Since he has been in and out of the hospital and lives alone, he believes his chances of eventually going to a nursing home are great. But it is not completely clear what his policy actually will cover, even though he pays $185 per month — a premium he can barely afford.

These are just two examples of policies failing to live up to people's expectations. The need for a national long-term care program is imperative.

However, until such a system is in place, seniors are left with few choices — they can "spend down" to a level where Medicaid pays for long-term care, or those who can afford it can purchase private long-term care insurance.

With today's health care costs soaring, minimum standards for the growing private long-term care insurance market are desperately needed. The number of people willing and able to purchase long-term care policies, while still relatively small, has doubled in the past two and a half years, and is likely to increase. Seniors need to know they are protected from the fraud and abuse often associated with long-term care insurance.

Certain Protections are Vital

These protections include such basic provisions as standardization of all long-term care insurance products, inflation protection, guaranteed renewability and counseling services.

There are several areas where reforms would be of particular importance to the consumer. For example, waiting periods due to pre-existing conditions such as a stroke or heart disease should be limited and clearly explained to consumers.

Likewise, new waiting periods should not be required for someone switching policies. Under new proposed federal guidelines, non-payment of premiums would be the only cause for the cancellation of an individual policy. Seniors must be assured their policy can be renewed no matter what their age or health condition.

Long-term care policy language also should be clear and simple, with standardized terms to improve understanding and ease comparison between policies. It is equally important that grants to states for insurance counseling be increased so seniors confused by insurance language have a place to turn.

Remaining in the home is the favored choice of most seniors needing long-term care. Given that some chronic illnesses, such as Parkinson's and Alzheimer's, do not necessarily need skilled care, insurance should offer coverage for both home and community-based care, allowing seniors more choice.

Inflation protection also is very important. Current long-term care policies can include inflation protection as an option.

However, it is essential that all policies offer inflation protection as a standard benefit since the cost of a nursing home bed, now anywhere from $45 to $200 a day, could double in a few years.

To protect seniors from unnecessarily high premium increases, the National Committee also urges that insurance companies be required to obtain state approval for rate increases.

In the case of long-term care, the National Committee believes federal standards are necessary to assure protection for consumers through better quality long-term care insurance polices.

Buying Long-Term Care Insurance

As a rule, long-term care insurance is not needed if your annual income is less than $15,000 and you have less than $50,000 in savings. If you do plan to buy a policy, here are some helpful hints:

- Take your time and compare several policies before making a decision.
- Check to be sure the insurance company has an A+ or A rating in the Annual A.M. Best Co. Insurance Review, available at local libraries. Also check the Better Business Bureau.
- If you don't understand what you are buying, ask for impartial help.
- Ask whether the policy meets or exceeds standards set by the National Association of Insurance Commissioners. You will want to be sure it covers Alzheimer's disease, requires no prior hospitalization and pays for custodial care as well as intermediate and skilled nursing care.

- Be sure the benefit is adequate. It doesn't need to cover the full cost, but you should be able to afford the remainder on your income. Also consider inflation protection.
- Once you've bought the policy, review it frequently. Don't be pressured into a change, however, and be sure to check any waiting periods or exclusions applicable to the new policy.

When Choosing a Nursing Home

Quality and payment issues require attention when choosing a nursing home. Yet, in many cases, individuals have very little choice and must accept whatever nursing home bed is available. Whether in the home of your choice or not, the most important key to quality care for your loved one is continued active involvement, love and support.

Speak up to support positive situations and to raise concerns in bad situations. Seek out other residents and family members. Get to know the staff. Make contact with your community's long-term care ombudsman and become familiar with the laws and regulations that apply to nursing home care.

Quality of Care Issues

Some quality issues are subjective while others are critical to any resident's health and well-being. Ask nursing home residents and their families, your physician, members of the clergy and others what they think about various facilities.

Visit as many nursing homes as possible. Visit again on the weekend or in the evening, when many homes reduce staff and services. Follow your instincts. Do you like what you see? Are residents out of bed during the day, dressed and happily occupied? Ask to have a meal with the residents. Is the dining room pleasant? Is the food good and nutritious? Do people who need assistance get it in a timely fashion? Do activities appeal to a range of interests and abilities? Is there a resident or family council? Are many residents physically restrained? Is rehabilitative and restorative care available routinely to residents in need?

Payment Issues

Most nursing home residents, even if they pay privately when they enter a home, run out of money because of the high costs. Then they convert to Medicaid payment. Unless you are certain you can pay indefinitely with private funds, choose a facility that accepts Medicaid payment, find out what your state's Medicaid eligibility rules are, and find out what residents' rights are or will be as a Medicaid nursing home resident.

Nursing homes which accept Medicaid cannot transfer you once you exhaust private funds. Federal law prohibits nursing homes from charging Medicaid residents or their families for items and services covered by Medicaid. It also prohibits homes from asking Medicaid beneficiaries for contributions as a condition of admission, or charging fees to supplement the Medicaid rate. Facilities must provide a list of what items and services are included in the basic Medicaid or private pay rate and any extra charges.

Getting Help

Contact the State Office on Aging for the name and number of the long-term care ombudsman program nearest you. Ombudsmen are empowered by law to serve as advocates for nursing home residents and assist with any complaints you have. 2/89

Family Members and Health Decisions

Some doctors and nurses ignore living wills, researchers at the University of North Carolina report.

In fact, medical treatment given to nursing home residents differed from care they had requested in their written living wills in 25 percent of the cases examined, the research showed. One possible explanation for the difference in treatment was suggested by Marion Danis and others in an article in the *New England Journal of Medicine*.

"The data suggest that in caring for incapacitated patients, physicians balance respect for [patient wishes] with other competing ethical principles to make what they believe are the wisest decisions," the article said.

Medical ethicists therefore recommend that individuals wishing to control their own treatment use a durable power of attorney instead. A durable power of attorney formally appoints a relative or friend to act as a proxy if the patient is incapacitated.

Unfortunately, most nursing home residents don't have either a durable power of attorney or a living will. Instead, nursing home residents tend to informally ask a son or daughter to make health decisions for them should they become incapacitated, says a study published in the February issue of *Archives of Internal Medicine*.

This means residents also need to know what kinds of treatment might be used in life-threatening situations, then decide whether they want them done, the article states.

ASK MARY JANE

Mary Jane Yarrington, a National Committee senior policy analyst with over 30 years experience handling Social Security and Medicare problems, responds each month in Saving Social Security to questions selected from the thousands of letters received from members seeking guidance or information.

• • •

Q. Did you know that Medicare is now paying for one lens when a cataract is removed? It's ludicrous! When I got my new glasses after surgery, the vision place took my old ones. When Medicare paid for only one lens, I was out of pocket $68. Please warn seniors not to give up their old glasses.

A. Thank you for alerting other seniors.

In 1990, Congress threatened to eliminate all coverage for eyeglasses after cataract surgery. The National Committee fought hard, together with Rep. Marilyn Lloyd, D-Tenn., and other members of Congress, to retain the Medicare payment.

The best we were able to achieve was a compromise. Medicare will continue to pay for a first pair of eyeglasses or contact lenses following cataract surgery, but seniors themselves must pay the full cost of future changes. There is no national policy, however, on Medicare payment for a full pair of eyeglasses or only a single contact lens following removal of a second cataract. Seniors ordering new glasses after a second surgery may wish to call Medicare ahead of time and ask about the payment policy before discarding old frames which are still usable. The change in Medicare payment for glasses following cataract surgery was based on the changed treatment of cataracts since Medicare became law.

An intraocular implant now usually replaces the natural lens; formerly special prescription eyeglasses compensated for the loss of the natural lens. Glasses or contact lenses now prescribed after an implant can be compared to corrective glasses or lenses prescribed for other seniors. As you may know, Medicare has never paid for regular eyeglasses or contacts. 11/91

Q. My mother never worked for a salary (she raised nine children), so she would be entitled to my father's Social Security checks if he dies before her, correct? Would she be entitled to his Social Security checks if he is in a nursing home or at a different address?

A. At or after age 60 (50 if disabled), your mother will be eligible for a widow benefit based on your father's Social Security earning record. If she is less than 65 when her widow benefit begins, it will be reduced for early retirement.

She will be entitled to a Social Security spouse benefit at or after age 62 if your father is receiving Social Security benefits. Again, her benefit would be reduced if she is less than 65 when her benefit begins. A different address would not matter.

If your father is in a nursing home, a residential care facility, or perhaps living with one of your siblings and your mother is managing his affairs, she may want to inquire at her local Social Security office about being made his representative payee. If your father becomes eligible for Medicaid, spousal impoverishment rules may permit your mother to receive all or part of his Social Security check for her support. 9/91

Q. I am 68, still working full time, and earning above average. When applying for Medicare, the Social Security representative started making out a benefit application. She said I may be able to receive three or four checks at the end of this year in spite of my salary. Please explain this to me. I did not know you could receive a good salary and draw benefits at the same time. Would it be better for me to wait until age 70 and get three percent more for waiting?

A. Follow the excellent advice given you by your Social Security office. In 1991, individuals over age 65 can earn $9,720 without losing any benefits. For each $3 of earnings above that amount, $1 of benefits is lost. But, if you are entitled to monthly benefits of $600, for example, you could earn $31,320 this year before all your benefits would be offset.

Provide your Social Security local office your best estimate of your 1991 earnings and correct that estimate if at any time during the year your anticipated earnings change appreciably. Social Security will determine how many months of benefits you can receive even though you continue to work and checks will begin in the appropriate month toward the end of the year.

If you advise Social Security that you intend to continue working, your benefits will stop in January and resume again toward the end of next year if your estimated 1992 earnings allow some months of benefits to be paid. Delayed retirement credits will be added effective next January for any months that benefits are not paid this year. However, since the added credits are not sufficient to make up for delaying benefits, it is to your advantage to apply for any benefits you have coming.

Two words of warning:
1. If you receive benefits while continuing to work at earnings over the limit, your actual earnings must be reported to Social Security prior to April 15 of the next year.

2. If you underestimate your earnings, any overpayment you receive will have to be repaid. However, if you overestimate your earnings, Social Security will automatically recompute and send you any additional benefits you are due. 9/91

Q. I am a disabled World War II veteran without a pension. We have only Social Security. I am 71 and need a hearing aid. Will Medicare pay for this? My wife has had heart surgery and has to have $60 to $70 of drugs each month so I hope we can get some help.

A. Medicare does not cover hearing aids. However, if your total household income this year is $7,578 or less, you may be eligible to have your state Medicaid program pay for your Medicare Part B premiums and co-payments. Your local Family Assistance Office can explain this program.

As a wartime veteran, you may be eligible for Veterans Administration assistance.

In 1990, a married veteran can receive pension benefits if his family income is less than $8,864; a single veteran, $6,767. Higher limits apply to veterans who are house bound or in need of aid and attendance.

Veterans with even higher income may qualify because not all income counts. The most important exclusion is annual medical expenses over five percent of basic pension amounts. As a married veteran, when you have paid over $443.20 for medical expenses this year, additional medical payments can reduce the amount of countable income and possibly entitle you to a pension.

Your combined 1990 Medicare Part B premiums of $686.40 and expected $700-800 in drug bills mean you and your wife are anticipating nearly $1,000 in excess medical payments this year, without counting anything else.

Under the veterans pension program you may also claim

other out-of-pocket medical expenses such as Medigap premiums, Medicare deductibles and co-payments, doctor, hospital and laboratory charges for which you are not reimbursed by insurance or Medicare, eyeglasses, hearing aids, wheelchairs, crutches, over-the-counter medicines, nursing home or home health care costs and even travel to and from a medical facility or doctor's office.

The Veterans Administration office can provide more information. Or seek help from a service officer with a veterans organization. The Disabled American Veterans, the American Legion and the Veterans of Foreign Wars all help veterans without charge whether or not they are members. 5/90

Q. My husband is 72 and he receives $291 a month from Social Security. I am 70 and receive $404 a month on my own work record. If my husband dies, do I receive any widow benefits besides my own Social Security benefits? If so, how much? If I should die first, is he entitled to widower benefits from my Social Security?

A. Husbands and wives are each eligible for their own Social Security benefits plus the difference, if any, between their own benefits and their spouse or widow(er) benefits. Since your Social Security benefits of $404 a month are greater than your husband's benefits, you would not be entitled to any additional benefits based on his Social Security earnings record.

If you die first, your husband could receive widower benefits. His own Social Security benefits plus widower benefits would equal the amount you were receiving at the time of your death. However, since your husband's benefits are quite low, he may have worked some years in employment not covered by Social Security. If he receives a public annuity for non-Social Security work, his widower benefits could be further reduced or totally offset. 5/90

Q. What happens to the taxes applied to a Social Security account if the person never accumulates the required quarters to become eligible for benefits? For example, in 1945, I became employed in Civil Service and remained in government service until retirement. But the Statement of Earnings Social Security sent me shows I have 26 quarters of coverage (i.e., Social Security work credits) for work between 1937 and 1950. I am 72 years old and probably never will be eligible for any Social Security benefits.

A. Payroll contributions of all workers and their employers are deposited directly into trust funds from which benefits are paid to all eligible individuals. The Social Security Administration maintains records of each worker's Social Security credits and earnings in order to determine benefit eligibility and the amount of monthly benefits. It does not, as many workers mistakenly believe, maintain personal "savings" accounts for each worker.

Based on your age, you need only two more Social Security work credits. If you were to earn $1,040 in 1990 in wages covered by Social Security, you would be eligible for minimum benefits beginning in January 1991. If you earn $1,040 or more this year, I suggest you take your 1990 W-2 statement of earnings to your local Social Security office and file for benefits as soon as possible after the first of the year. Eligibility for benefits will, of course, also make you eligible for Medicare if you do not already have eligibility either from post-1982 Federal employment or through a spouse's Social Security earnings record. 7/90

Q. We've been divorced three years. I am 69 and he is 81. I retired at 62 and receive my own Social Security plus part of his. He now gets almost $700, but I get only $279. I pay $60 a month for my HMO. Believe me, I don't want food stamps or SSI ($74), but without it I would die. Why can't I draw more of his Social Security?

A. Sorry to say, Social Security spouse benefits cannot exceed half of a wage earner's full benefits. And when you began receiving benefits at age 62, both your own benefits and your spouse benefits had to be reduced for early retirement. Upon your former husband's death, however, you will be entitled to 100 percent of the Social Security benefits he is receiving at that time.

You don't mention Medicaid. Beginning January 1991, individuals with limited assets and below poverty level income are entitled to have their Medicare Part B premiums, co-payments and deductible paid by their state Medicaid program. Some states also pay monthly HMO fees. I urge you to contact your local social service agency or health department and ask about Medicaid assistance. 4/91

Q. I have a 67-year-old lady friend who has been denied benefits based on her divorced husband's earnings record.

They were married more than 20 years. Each time she visits the Social Security office, the representative tells her she cannot get spouse benefits or Medicare until her ex-husband retires and turns 65. He is younger and still working. She does not know his exact date of birth. When she asks, they refuse to give it to her. Can you assist with this problem?

A. Since she has been divorced more than two years, your friend will be eligible for spouse benefits and Medicare when her former husband reaches age 62, whether or not he ceases working at that time.

Your friend should just ask when she will be eligible for

benefits as his divorced spouse. The Social Security office can give her that information. 5/91

Q. I worked until I was 72, paying maximum Social Security tax. When I retired, I received Social Security benefits based on additional earnings. However, my wife, who began receiving benefits at 65, receives considerably less than one-half of my benefits. Is that correct or has Social Security made an error?

A. The Social Security Act does not provide for a wife to share in delayed retirement credits her husband earns by working past full retirement age. That is why your wife's benefits are less than half of yours.

The maximum a wife may receive is half of her husband's benefits determined as if he were 65 when he retired. That rule applies whether he is 62 or 72 when his benefits begin.

However, when and if she is widowed, your wife will receive the full amount you are receiving at the time of your death, including the delayed retirement credits you earned by working until age 72. 5/91

Q. I retired at age 67 in 1985. I did not apply for Medicare at 65 because I was fully covered by a medical care policy at work. I didn't realize I was being penalized by paying more for Medicare until this January when I received the annual notice of Social Security and Medicare payments. I called Social Security and they said nothing could be done. I wrote to my Congressman and again, no help was available. Who can help me get my penalty removed?

A. Contrary to the information you have been given, delayed enrollment penalties can be removed if they were applied in error. Not only that, premium surcharges can be

Make Every Voice Count

refunded for all the years they have been paid. All that is needed is verification you were actively employed and were covered by your employer's plan between your 65th birthday and the month you enrolled for Medicare. Penalties cannot be waived for months before January 1983, but that does not affect you because you reached 65 after the waiver became effective.

You should contact your former employer and request an affidavit stating you were covered by an employer health insurance plan from prior to your 65th birthday through the month you filed for Medicare (specify any break in employer insurance coverage.) Include insurer's name, group policy number and coverage dates, if known.

Take the affidavit to your local Social Security office and request an adjustment of premiums to remove the surcharge and a refund of previously overpaid contributions for any months you had employer health insurance while actively employed. 6/91

Q. My husband chose not to receive his benefits until age 70. We received our first checks Nov. 4, 1989. I was almost 63. My question is this: Should I have applied for spouse benefits at age 62 and, if so, is there any way I can recover the lost benefits? I have tried unsuccessfully to find out about this and hope you might help.

A. You suffered no loss of benefits. Unless you were eligible for Social Security based on your own earnings, you were not eligible until your husband began to receive his benefits.

Moreover, when spouse benefits begin before age 65, they must be reduced to make up for the longer time in which benefits will be paid. Your spouse benefits were reduced 18 percent because your benefits began 26 months before you would attain age 65. Had you started receiving spouse benefits in the month you became 62, they would have been reduced 25 percent. 8/91

Q. My husband died in November 1986. We were married from April 1977 until his death. Will I be able to collect his Social Security benefit?

A. Widow benefits are payable if a marriage lasts at least nine months before ending in death, or even less if the death is accidental or a child was born of the marriage. A 10-year marriage requirement applies only in cases of divorce.

If you are not remarried — or if you do not remarry before age 60 — you will be eligible for widow benefits on your deceased husband's earning record. Full widow benefits are payable at age 65, reduced widow benefits as early as 60 (50 if disabled). 8/91

Q. My wife retired at age 65. She went blind, just overnight, when she was 70. The question I would like answered: Is my wife entitled to any more on her retirement claim since she is totally blind? As of this date she gets $414 a month.

A. Like other workers whose careers are cut short by severe disabilities, workers who become blind are eligible for Social Security disability insurance benefits even though they may not yet have reached retirement age. However, there is no provision in the law to increase benefits due to disability or blindness which occur after retirement.

Monthly Social Security benefits, whether paid to retired workers or to blind or disabled workers, are determined on the worker's average earnings over the number of years that must be counted. Once benefits begin, they are generally

Make Every Voice Count

increased only by cost-of-living adjustments (COLAs). However, benefits also may increase if the worker returns to the work force. 8/91

Q. I was under the impression that Social Security medical benefits could be drawn when a person is unable to work and has no other income. Since last June, I have had four heart catheterizations, three angioplasties and a double bypass. My own insurance hardly paid anything. Please let me know how the medical part of Social Security works.

A. The Social Security medical benefit program, or Medicare, is hospital and medical insurance protection for individuals age 65 and over who are eligible for Social Security cash benefits. Disabled workers also can be eligible for Medicare, but only after they have been receiving Social Security disability benefits for 24 months. Since you are newly disabled and are younger than 65, you are not yet eligible.

If you have limited resources, however, you may be eligible for Medicaid, which is a program of medical assistance jointly funded by the state and federal government, but administered by the state. I suggest you contact your local Medicaid office, family service agency, or health department and ask about eligibility for assistance with your medical expenses. You should find these agencies listed in the government section of your phone book. 8/91

Q. I retired at age 56 and began receiving Social Security benefits at age 62. A year later, I suffered a stroke affecting my entire left side. Because I was two quarters shy of having worked five out of the 10 years prior to applying for disability benefits, I was denied. I paid Social Security taxes for almost 40 years. It doesn't seem fair I am denied an extra $100 a month simply because I needed to retire early. Is there a loophole? Being sick is expensive!

A. Social Security Disability Insurance is somewhat like term insurance. That is, a worker is insured while working regularly and up to five years after work ceases. When a worker no longer has Social Security work credits in at least 20 calendar quarters out of the 40 quarters ending when disability begins, he or she is no longer insured for Social Security disability benefits. Congress imposed this recency-of-work requirement in order to limit disability benefits to persons who left the work force as a result of disability.

Though the recency-of-work test seems inappropriate for someone with a 40-year work history, I know no "loophole" which would help you qualify. 8/91

Q. I was married 25 years when I divorced my first husband. I heard I'm entitled to part of his Social Security retirement. I am 72, he is 70. I don't get any answer from Social Security. I'm not married at this time. I would appreciate some kind of an answer.

A. Since you were married for more than ten years before you were divorced and are not now married, you are eligible for divorced spouse benefits on your first husband's earning record. If you did not receive any Social Security benefits before age 65, your spouse benefits would be fifty percent of your former husband's full benefits. However, spouse benefits (or widow benefits if your former husband predeceases you) are payable only to the extent that they exceed your own benefits. In other words, you are eligible to receive your own benefits plus the difference, if any, between your own full benefits and the benefits you are eligible to receive as a spouse or as a widow. You cannot receive both.

If you are not satisfied you are receiving all the benefits

to which you are entitled, you should file a claim on your first husband's earnings record. Social Security will then be required to furnish you a written decision. 2/90

Q. As a World War II veteran with combat service in the European Theatre, 3-1/2 years in the Army, am I entitled to any additional benefits under the Social Security program?

A. Military service was not covered by Social Security until 1957, but veterans who served from 1940 through 1956 can receive free Social Security credits for military service if using military credits provides higher monthly Social Security benefits. Pre-1957 military service, however, may not be used for Social Security if it is counted for Federal Civil Service retirement.

You also may be eligible for veterans benefits through the U.S. Department of Veterans Affairs or through a state veterans' assistance program. Phone numbers for federal, state or county veterans' agencies should be found in your local telephone directory. Veterans' service organizations such as the Disabled American Veterans, American Legion or Veterans of Foreign Wars are good sources of information as well as assistance with application.

Editor's note: Because monthly Social Security benefits usually are greater if only post-1950 earnings are needed, credits for military service prior to 1951 are seldom counted. 10/90

Q. My husband and I have been together for 40 years and have raised a family, but we never married. If he dies before me, can I get his Social Security as I have no other income?

A. Only if you are considered his legal widow. Few states now recognize common-law marriages, but in the past, many

Make Every Voice Count

did. Social Security follows state law, so if at any time during the years you have lived as man and wife your state (or a state in which you then resided) recognized your union as a common-law marriage, Social Security regards you as married. But it will be up to you to prove you lived as man and wife while a common-law statute was in effect.

As a wife you are entitled to spouse benefits at age 62 and widow benefits upon your husband's death. However, if your union is not recognized as a marriage, you will not be entitled to either spouse or widow Social Security benefits. I urge you to seek legal advice to determine your marital status. 12/91

Q. I am a widow with a daughter who has cystic fibrosis. I'm told I lose my Social Security when she turns 16, though she will keep hers until 19 if she stays in school. There are times when she needs four treatments a day when she gets sick. I cannot work and care for her, but there is no way we can make it on her Social Security alone. Any advice?

A. Social Security mother benefits ordinarily stop when the youngest child reaches age 16. But that is not true if a child is so disabled as to meet Social Security's definition of disabled adult child. In fact, if your daughter is severely disabled, remains disabled, and does not marry, Social Security benefits can continue to her for life and to you as long as she is in your care.

If her doctor indicates your daughter's disability is severe, about six months before her 16th birthday, contact Social Security and file an application for continuation of mother benefits based on her disability. Social Security will tell you what medical evidence you need to submit in support of your application and will make a determination as to your eligibility. 12/91

Q. I've spent 34 years in the work force and want to know how much Social Security I've built up so far. I'm 59 now and intend to work until 65. Could you please refer me to the correct agency?

A. Social Security provides an earnings history and benefit estimate to anyone who asks. Just call Social Security at their new 800 number — 1-800-772-1213 — and request an application for a Personal Earnings and Benefit Estimate Statement. When the application arrives, complete and mail it. In about a month you will receive an estimate of how much you can expect to receive as a monthly Social Security benefit at ages 62, 65, and 70.

The report also will provide a year-by-year record of all earnings credited to your Social Security account number. An earnings record, by the way, should be checked every two years so that corrections, if necessary, can be made within the legal limit of three years, three and a half months after the year of earnings. There are some exceptions to this three-year rule, but corrections can be made most easily from recent personal and payroll tax records. 12/91

Q. I am writing to ask if I can claim my deceased wife's Social Security benefits. She passed away 19 years ago after working for more than 20 years. I retired at 62 and am now 77.

A. If you had recently lost your wife, I would suggest you call Social Security's 800 number to receive an immediate answer. However, since your wife has been deceased for

Make Every Voice Count

many years, her earning record will not be readily available on a tele-service computer. Therefore, it is probably best to contact your local Social Security office directly.

Within a few days, your local office can let you know if the survivor benefit you are entitled to receive on your wife's earnings record is greater than the benefit you are now receiving. If so, you are entitled to receive the difference as a widower benefit. If you want a formal determination rather than an oral report, file an application for survivor benefit and Social Security will respond with a written decision as to whether or not you are eligible for additional benefits as a widower. 12/91

THE BEST OF "HEALTH TALK"

The National Committee believes the government should take good care of its citizens. But it also believes we've all got to take good care of ourselves. So in every issue of Saving Social Security, *they publish a popular column called "Health Talk," featuring the latest health information. In the following chapters, you'll find a healthy helping of advice from these columns.*

• • •

Eat and Exercise Your Way to Health

Eating right, a little exercise and a little caution can help keep you happy, healthy, and looking and feeling great — inside and out.

Most Americans Lack Good Diet Knowledge

Most Americans wrongly believe the foods they eat and drink are healthy, a federal survey of food consumption shows. Actually, the "average" diet is too high in fat and salt, too low in fiber and not adequately varied.

Federal research shows about one in three American adults has high blood pressure. If they were to restrict their salt and sodium, their blood pressure usually would fall.

Too Little Good Food

The Diet and Health Knowledge Survey, a nationwide poll on knowledge and attitudes which may affect food choices, questioned meal planners and preparers in about 1,300 American homes.

Sugar, like salt, can be found naturally in many foods. Fruits, vegetables and milk products, although they contain sugar, are important sources of vitamins, minerals and fiber. However, processed sugars — white sugar, honey, corn sweeteners, molasses, brown sugar and fructose — provide calories and little else.

Read labels to learn how much salt or sugar is in a product. The words "salt," "soda" or "sodium" usually mean a product is high in sodium. Also, ingredients are listed in order by weight — from greatest to least. If sugar is one of the first three ingredients or if several forms of sugar are listed, the product is probably high in sugar.

New Nutrition Guidelines

Americans only eat about half the recommended servings of fruits and vegetables each day. The government now recommends at least three servings of vegetables and two of fruit daily. It also suggests at least six servings of grain products — bread, cereals, pasta and rice — preferably whole grains. Dietary fiber can reduce the symptoms of chronic constipation, diverticular disease and hemorrhoids.

American diets lack the variety needed to supply recommended amounts of several of the more than 40 different nutrients needed for good health. A variety of foods

— not highly fortified foods or supplements — is the right way to get nutrients.

The guideline has several recommendations on nutrition and health:

- Eat a variety of foods.
- Maintain a healthy weight.
- Choose a diet low in fat and cholesterol.
- Eat plenty of vegetables, fruits and grains.
- Use sugars only in moderation.
- Use salt and sodium only in moderation.
- If you drink alcohol, do so in moderation.

For more information or a free copy of the Dietary Guideline, write the Consumer Information Center, Department 514-X, Pueblo, Colo. 81009. 4/91

Healthy Food Choices

The study of the nutritional needs of the elderly is a new field, but according to Health Media of America, age related changes in body composition and metabolism require seniors to keep a sharp eye on their food choices. Too many seniors are undernourished from eating processed and refined foods, from reduced metabolism, diminished appetite and from the effects of medication. Metabolic changes, along with decreased physical activity, require obtaining the same amount of nutrients from a lower caloric level. There is little room for "empty" calories.

According to health officials, of particular concern to seniors should be B vitamins, zinc, and calcium. An estimated 30 percent of seniors lose their ability to make stomach acid, which interferes with the absorption of vitamin B12 and folic acid. Studies suggest that deficiencies in these, as well as in B6, can cause neurological changes such as a decline in alertness, loss of memory, and numbness of the extremities. B2, or riboflavin, aids in the release of energy from carbohydrates, proteins and fats. A deficiency in zinc can cause diminished taste sensation, low appetite, and delays in healing wounds.

Since bones tend to weaken with age, seniors require at least 1500 milligrams of calcium a day. Due to lack of exposure to the sun, seniors may not get as much Vitamin D, essential to the absorption of calcium and phosphorus, as they should.

Some doctors recommend getting these nutrients from wise food choices, rather than supplements. A recent study shows no evidence that small doses of supplements are beneficial, and large doses can be harmful. Another reason to get nutrients from food is the absorption rate is much higher. Taking a calcium supplement might result in only 20% absorption, while drinking milk renders 45%.

Dark green leafy vegetables, whole grain and enriched cereals, pastas, breads, beans and peas are good sources of vitamins B2 (riboflavin) and B6. Other good sources of vitamin B6 are fish, poultry, avocados, bananas, nuts and potatoes. Meat, fish, milk, oysters and nutritional yeast are good sources of B12. Calcium is found in milk and dairy products, sardines, canned salmon with bones, dark green leafy vegetables, citrus fruits, and dried peas and beans. Meat, eggs, poultry, seafood, liver, milk and whole grains are rich in zinc.

To simplify, remember the Mediterranean diet of southern Italy, which is rich in fish, lentils, grains, vegetables and olive oil. Not only are they vitamin-rich alternatives to the over-processed American diet, southern Italians boast one of the lowest heart-disease rates in the world. 5/89

Controlling Your Cholesterol

A hearty breakfast of eggs, breakfast meat and toast with butter. A sandwich covered with mayonnaise, or a fast-food burger and fries. Meat and vegetables laden with cream sauce or butter.

If this sounds like your diet, you may have high cholesterol.

High cholesterol is increasingly blamed for a myriad of health problems, including high blood pressure and heart disease. Small amounts of cholesterol are produced naturally by the body, but most cholesterol is ingested — and the average American's diet contains too much fat and cholesterol.

You don't have to be obese to have a cholesterol problem. Conversely, your body may be overweight but you may not have a cholesterol problem. It all depends on your metabolism — and your genes.

But, if you don't have the right genes, you can compensate with the proper diet.

Start by cutting back on butter and oils. Use margarine instead of butter, preferably one made with an all vegetable oil high in polyunsaturates. Beware of palm and cottonseed oils! These are high in saturated fats, and are used in processing many cookies, crackers and chips. If you are confused about the oils, remember this rule of thumb — the more solid the fat when refrigerated, the higher it is in saturated fat.

Reduce your consumption of fatty meats, including pork and well-marbled beef. Eat chicken and fish instead. Buy lean hamburger with the lowest percentage of fat. Avoid frying foods — try roasting, broiling or microwaving instead. Skim the fat off gravies and soups.

Fast foods are generally very high in fat, so it's best to cut back, particularly on burgers and fries. Even ordinary restaurants serve foods that are high in fat. For instance, cream sauces, gravies, casseroles and souffles are often fat and cholesterol-laden, as are most meats, salad dressings and desserts.

Eggs are a high source of cholesterol, as is liver. There

are egg substitutes on the market, and these can be used in most recipes calling for eggs. Most dairy products are high in fat but low-fat products are also available.

There are some foods that are believed to be helpful in the battle against cholesterol, such as tofu, oatmeal and fish oil, but none of them has been scientifically proven to lower cholesterol.

Many people report that their cholesterol levels return to acceptable levels within a few months of their diet changes. For those who still have problems even after their diet is changed, doctors do have cholesterol lowering drugs. But the best medicine for cholesterol problems is prevention. Eat smart and live longer! 3/88

"Good" Cholesterol Helpers

Evidence indicates that keeping up levels of cholesterol known as high-density lipoproteins (HDL, or "good" cholesterol) is as important to health as keeping low density lipoproteins (LDL) down. How large a role HDL plays in the complex lipid transport system is not known, but it carries excess LDL to the liver for destruction.

While limiting one's intake of saturated fats can lower the total cholesterol count, additional dietary changes can raise the HDL level. One is substituting olive oil for corn and soy oil. While switching to vegetable oils generally reduces total cholesterol counts, only olive oil does not suppress HDLs. Soluble fibers such as oat and rice, acting as cholesterol carriers, also lower total cholesterol. Several recent long-term studies reveal 1-1/2 to 4 ozs. of oat bran daily raises HDL levels 10-15%. Substituting fish for red meat has long been touted as the healthier choice for reducing total cholesterol. And the fatty acids found in oily fishes raise HDL levels.

Vitamins play a role as well: Recent U.S. Department of

Agriculture research shows the richer blood is in vitamin C and niacin, a common B vitamin, the higher the HDL level. Zinc, however, has been shown to significantly reduce HDL levels, according to a recent article in the *American Journal of Clinical Nutrition*.

In addition to dietary changes, losing weight (if one is overweight) and regular exercise boost HDLs. For those people with serious risk of heart disease, the prescription drug gemfibrozil (Lopid) has been shown to lift HDLs as well.

Though the reason behind the benefits of raising one's HDL level is still unclear, the encouraging evidence suggests there is no reason to wait for the definitive answer. The studies reinforce what is already known: Eating less saturated fats is good for the heart. 3/89

Exercise May Be Crucial for Senior Health

Seniors who exercise regularly may live better and longer. Having many disabilities in later years is due not so much to the aging process, but to the reversible deterioration of muscle mass which results from a sedentary lifestyle, according to data on frail seniors gathered at eight sites selected by the National Institute on Aging.

"At least 50 percent of our longevity of life expectancy is related to lifestyle, not genetics," says Robert N. Butler, M.D., the original director of the National Institute on Aging.

How to Begin

Always check with your doctor before beginning an exercise program. Even when an exercise program is undertaken later in life, it still can help regain lost strength and agility. A beginning program may include low-intensity leisure activities such as gardening, golfing and walking, since they require no expensive equipment and lead to few injuries.

Exercisers over 50 need to take special precautions. The Strength Connection by Kenneth Cooper, M.D., recommends good breathing technique while performing strength training exercises. A yearly physical examination also is recommended. In addition, exercising seniors should:
- Take extra time to warm up and cool down.
- Start slowly and progress gradually.
- Work with a partner or group for safety.

Many exercises can be done at home. Strength training exercises using devices which adjust the resistance to equal the force applied are ideal for arthritis sufferers.

For more information on exercise and seniors, call or write the National Exercise For Life Institute, P.O. Box 2000, Excelsior, Minn. 55331-9967, (612) 448-3094. 5/91

Balanced Fitness is Trend of the '90s

While aerobic exercise was popular in the 1980s, balanced fitness — a program involving all body parts — is the exercise trend for the 1990s. Geriatric physical therapists say seniors have undertaken a wellness-oriented lifestyle which often includes regular exercise and sports.

This new lifestyle often is adopted in an effort to remain independent as long as possible. Out-of-pocket medical costs also can be reduced by living a more healthy lifestyle.

Research shows regular exercise at all ages improves muscle strength, cardiovascular fitness, physical endurance and flexibility.

For older Americans, exercise also can prevent bone loss — osteoporosis — an ailment common to about half of all American women over 45.

Make Every Voice Count

Reprinted With Special Permission of North American Syndicate, Inc.

Drugs and Technology... Your Expanding Medical Options

Medical technology is advancing at an increasingly rapid rate. More drugs and medical technology are available than ever before. The National Committee wants to help its members, in partnership with their physicians, make the best possible choices.

Prescription Drugs... Handle With Care

Many sudden and unusual health problems can be caused by prescription medicines either improperly prescribed or misused. That's why after beginning a new drug it is important to note any effects. If you notice dizziness, vomiting, confusion, difficulty keeping your balance, or any other new symptom, contact your physician immediately. Otherwise, be sure to follow your doctor's instructions. Don't take it just when you feel bad. And be sure to return to the doctor for a follow-up exam.

Mixing drugs is a serious problem and one that is more likely to affect the elderly, since they often may take more than one prescription drug. Also, the aging process leaves the body more vulnerable to adverse effects. For example, kidney function decreases, slowing the body's ability to remove toxins, and there is less water in tissue to dilute the drug. Often the proper dose for a young person is too high for an older person.

Mixing Drugs Can Be Hazardous

One drug for hypertension, another for heart disease, a painkiller for arthritis — combined, these drugs can cause serious side effects that might not appear if one of the drugs was taken alone. Even an over-the-counter drug mixed with a prescription drug can cause adverse side effects. To be safe, always tell your doctor about all your medications, including any over-the-counter drugs you may be taking, even aspirin.

Sharing drugs is dangerous. Drugs are individually prescribed after careful consideration of the patient's age, weight, medical history, severity of illness, plus many other factors. A person using medicine meant for a friend's heart condition may find the prescription either too strong or too weak. They may easily develop side effects that the friend doesn't, or the drug may interact with one already being taken. Only a doctor or pharmacist can determine how drugs interact with each other, and with the patient's body.

Respect Non-Prescription Drugs

Never begin taking a prescription or non-prescription drug without first consulting a doctor about possible interaction with drugs you may already be taking. Like sharing drugs, treating a condition on your own could worsen it or cause other symptoms. Even some over-the-counter drugs can cause side effects if you have heart disease, high blood pressure, or other illnesses. So be sure to read information accompanying any drug. And talk to your doctor.

And, just as patients should never begin treatment on their own, they should not end treatment until advised by their doctor. Symptoms of some illnesses may seem to disappear after a few doses of a drug, even though an infection or other ailment is still present in the body. All doses of a medication should be taken as prescribed in order to completely cure an illness. 6/88

New Drug Therapies For Heart Attacks

New drugs can stop or limit the damage of a heart attack, but only if the patient gets help immediately, experts say. Once the flow of blood to a portion of the heart is blocked for several hours, the damage is irreversible.

Knowing the symptoms, which can be wide-ranging and confusing, is extremely important. So is knowing risk factors, such as obesity, diabetes, high blood pressure and family history.

Typical symptoms of a heart attack include a crushing pain in the chest, sweating, difficulty breathing, weakness and pain in the arms — particularly the left. Symptoms one could attribute to something else can cause devastating delays in seeking treatment. These include feelings of indigestion, back, shoulder and neck pain, and nausea. Early signs of trouble may appear during physical activity and disappear with rest. Any numbness or tingling of the fingers or toes, dizziness, shortness of breath or difficulty in breathing should not be ignored, experts advise.

Influenza Vaccination an Annual Must

An influenza vaccination is no more likely to cause side effects than a placebo, says a study recently published in the *Journal of The American Medical Association*. So with flu season right around the corner, experts are once again recommending that seniors be vaccinated.

Fear of developing flu-like symptoms from the shot is a major reason some people don't get immunized. But experts agree senior citizens benefit greatly from the vaccination. Influenza is still a disease to be reckoned with; it greatly increases the risk of developing pneumonia. The Centers for Disease Control estimates 25,725 people died from flu or pneumonia between October and May 1989.

Experts advise that it's necessary to be immunized annually because the viruses change from year to year. 10/90

Pneumococcal Vaccines

Pneumococcal vaccines are also available nationwide. The vaccine protects against bacteremia, meningitis, and pneumonia. All three diseases are potential killers, and pneumonia is the sixth leading cause of death in the United States. Medical experts advise that all older persons, and especially those with chronic illnesses, those who are bedridden, or those undergoing lengthy hospital stays, should be immunized.

Experts agree the vaccine need be given only once during a lifetime for continuous protection. The pneumonia vaccine is effective on 90 percent of pneumococci bacteria and is reimbursable under Medicare. Pneumococcal vaccines are also available at county health departments.

Sleeping Pills May be Harmful

One of the most often prescribed medications for seniors is a variety of sedative-hypnotics — otherwise known as sleeping pills. Yet experts believe side effects of these medications are not as benevolent as previously believed — leading one public health advocacy group to call for stricter warnings on one of the much prescribed drugs.

The top three sedatives on the market today, Halcion, Dalmane and Restoril, are in the same chemical classification as Valium and Librium, and while they do not share these drugs' publicized side effects, their own effects are not to be dismissed. The Public Citizen Health Research Group recently has called on the Food and Drug Administration to require stricter warnings on Halcion, the most widely prescribed sedative available.

Halcion, popular because it doesn't linger in the body and cause grogginess in the morning, has been known to cause amnesia, anxiety, aggression and other behavior problems. The drug has a risk of adverse side effects from eight up to 45 times higher than its chemical counterparts, according to Dr. Jerry Alvorn of Harvard Medical School.

Rather than automatically reaching for a pill, experts recommend trying to discern the cause of insomnia. For example, arthritic pain could be the culprit and better treated with anti-inflammatory drugs. And medications for other problems such as high blood pressure could cause sleeplessness.

Ibuprofen Linked With Kidney Failure

The pain reliever ibuprofen has been found to cause kidney failure in those with mild kidney disease, reported the journal *Annals of Internal Medicine*. The drug, marketed under such brand names as Motrin, Advil, Medipren and Nuprin, has been approved for non-prescription sale since 1985. Ibuprofen accounts for more than 20 percent of the nation's over-the-counter pain reliever sales. The drug's active ingredient, however, constricts blood flow and can cause problems for persons whose blood flow to the kidneys is already reduced by kidney, heart or liver damage or by aging, according to the article.

Space Program Provides Medical Technology

New ideas and new products — both big and small — have come out of America's space program — Tang® breakfast drink and Velcro® fasteners, to name just two. But for seniors, some of the most important contributions come when space technology is married to medical devices.

Using 25 years of research and technology gleaned by the National Aeronautics and Space Administration, private corporations, government agencies and academic institutions constantly seek to develop high-tech answers to medical questions.

Implants Use Wireless Technology

Frequently, NASA modifies existing devices for use in space. When these modifications are applied to medical devices — especially those implanted in the human body to replace or supplement an organ or gland — it gives the user more freedom to lead a normal life. These high-tech implants usually are smaller than their predecessors and can be recharged through the skin, eliminating the need for surgery to replace a battery every 18 months to two years.

One major spin-off of the space program is the programmable cardiac pacemaker — a device used to correct an irregular heartbeat. Based on NASA technology developed to send instructions to unmanned satellites, pacemakers now have two-way communications capability.

A physician can program a patient's pacemaker over the telephone, fine-tuning it to meet each individual's needs. When programming is complete, the pacemaker sends back a copy of the new settings so a permanent record can be made, says Pacesetter Systems, Inc., one manufacturer of the device.

Since the first pacemaker was implanted in 1973, improved technology has allowed manufacturers to miniaturize the pacemaker from its original 6 ozs. to its present 2 ounces. It has extended the device's lifetime another 10 to 20 years. Today's pacemakers also are immune to electrical interference caused by microwave ovens, which can stop conventional pacemakers. About 120,000 pacemakers have been implanted in the U.S. and more than 250,000 worldwide, Pacesetter System officials say.

Technology Makes Medication Easier

Thanks to space technology, a programmable, implantable medication system may reach the marketplace within the next year. The device will automatically administer the proper dosage of medication — just when the body needs it. The pump is designed not only to deliver accurate amounts of medication, within a milliliter at a time, but also to allow the patient to change his or her own dosage.

The cosmetic compact-size item contains not only enough medication to last up to three months, but a tiny infusion pump, a tube leading to the target area of the body, a battery and the computerized programming system to get in where it is needed. When medication runs low, the patient returns to the doctor for a refill. This is done by a hypodermic injection through the infusion pump's self-sealing membrane.

Make Every Voice Count

FRANK AND ERNEST ⓒby Bob Thaves

> TWENTY DOLLARS! LAST WEEK THIS MEDICINE COST ONLY FIFTEEN DOLLARS.
>
> WE DISCOVERED SOME NEW SIDE EFFECTS.
>
> PRESCRIPTIONS

Reprinted By Permission of NEA, Inc.

Diseases of Special Concern to Seniors

Unfortunately, one of the side effects of getting older is having to deal with the many ailments to which seniors are particularly susceptible. The National Committee makes every effort to encourage research on such diseases, and provides useful information as it becomes available.

Sleep Disorders

Complaints about sleeplessness and waking up still tired are symptoms of sleep disorders often associated with aging.

Sleep disturbances afflict many seniors — more than half of those at home and about two-thirds of those in long-term care facilities.

Sleep problems may be caused by retirement and changes in social patterns, death of a spouse or close friends, increased use of medications, and/or diseases and changes in heart rhythms.

As a person ages, his sleep patterns change. He gets less of the deeper stages of sleep and more of the lighter ones. Older people wake up more frequently — sometimes as many as 150 times a night.

Three major sleep complaints are excessive sleepiness, insomnia and strange or unusual behavior during sleep. Of these, insomnia is the most common for seniors.

Insomnia may be caused by depression, prescribed or over-the-counter medication or a medical condition. Shift work, traveling through different time zones or changes in daily routine or sleep patterns also may affect a senior's ability to get a good night's sleep.

Rather than using the quiet of the bedroom to let one's mind race and worry about life's problems, the American Sleep Disorders Association recommends seniors designate a day light period as "worry time." A person can use this time to list everything that's bothering them and write down possible solutions.

Worry often leads to depression, which then becomes a way of life for some. Many with symptoms of depression respond well to a number of medications, particularly when accompanied by counseling.

Insomniacs also complain pain, fever, itching or coughing keeps them awake. Many medications are available for these chronic conditions which may abruptly awaken a senior.

Watch What You Take in Before You Turn in

Experts at the Sleep Disorder Association recommend seniors with sleeping problems avoid drinking fluids — particularly alcohol or caffeine — before bed. They also caution against using sleeping pills to induce sleep. Because seniors metabolize and eliminate drugs less efficiently, the sleepy effect often continues until the next day. Also, using sleeping pills while taking other medications can cause adverse effects.

Many retired seniors have too much free time on their hands and, consequently, may sleep during the day. A 1988

Gallup survey found active retirees had fewer sleep problems than those less active. "Try to confine sleep to night time or nap time," say experts at the American Sleep Disorders Association.

Sometimes a senior's body tells him it's bedtime earlier than he wishes, often well before 9 p.m. Other seniors have success in delaying their bedtime, but not their waking time.

For a free copy of *Sleep As We Grow Older*, write the National Sleep Disorders Foundation, 122 South Robertson Blvd., Suite 201, Los Angeles, California, 90048. 6/91

Incontinence...Avoidable and Treatable

A recent National Institutes of Health conference has shed new light on urinary incontinence, the involuntary release of urine which afflicts at least 10 million American adults. Doctors attending the conference agreed that incontinence is *not* a normal consequence of aging, and is often treatable.

Incontinence is a symptom of other physical problems, rather than a disease in and of itself, according to the conference statement. Possible causes of incontinence include reactions to medication, menopause, surgery in the uro-genital regions, prostate disease, and lack of exercise. Twice as many women as men are incontinent.

The conference panel agreed that the high incidence of incontinence can be partly blamed on health care providers who ignore it and do not provide adequate diagnosis and treatment. Nonetheless, the panel recommended that any person with symptoms of incontinence contact their doctor for possible treatment, and called for a major research initiative to improve assessment and treatment of the problem. 12/88

Four Million With Alzheimer's Disease

A Harvard Medical School study has revealed that more than four million Americans over the age of 65 may have Alzheimer's disease, a figure double previous estimates. The rate increases dramatically for those over the age of 85.

Researchers say 10 percent of the 3,626 people studied "probably" had Alzheimer's and 18.7 percent between the ages of 75 and 85 were afflicted. That the number of those affected over 85 jumped 47 percent shows the disease rate rises with age, more so than previously suspected.

Alzheimer's disease is a degenerative disease of the nervous system with no known cause or cure. Symptoms include loss of memory, problems with speech and mobility and increasing dementia.

It's not just the patients who suffer, however; studies show the caregivers are more susceptible to prolonged emotional and physical stress and may, as a result, be more vulnerable to infectious diseases. Often, the caregiver is of advanced age as well, and suffering from age-related infirmities such as arthritis, or is an adult child with his/her own family to care for.

The Alzheimer's Disease and Related Disorders Association predicts 14 million people will be afflicted by the year 2040. National Institutes of Health Deputy Director Gene Cohen says the numbers alone make it "one of the biggest public-health dilemmas we've ever encountered." Most of these patients will eventually be institutionalized at great cost. Experts agree research to find the cause and a cure must be a top priority.

On an upbeat note, federal funds allocated to Alzheimer's research in 1989 was $123.4 million, compared with $5.1

million in 1978.

For more information, contact: The Alzheimer's Association, 70 East Lake Street, Suite 600, Chicago, Ill., 60601. 2/90

Breast Cancer Screening Guidelines

Eleven major medical organizations, including the American Medical Association and the National Cancer Institute (NCI), have agreed to recommend that women, ages 40 to 49, have routine mammograms, whether or not they show symptoms of breast cancer.

The guidelines recommend that women 40 to 49 receive a clinical exam annually and a mammogram every one or two years. At 50, both the clinical exam and mammogram should be performed yearly. These guidelines are for asymptomatic women only — those with signs of breast cancer or a family history of the disease should consult their doctor.

These screening guidelines are significant because early detection is key to survival. The five-year survival rate in early, localized cancer is 90 percent, but once cancer spreads outside of the breast it drops to 60 percent.

A 1988 NCI study found 24 percent fewer breast cancer deaths among women ages 40 to 49 who had regular mammograms.

Breast cancer is second only to lung cancer in cancer-caused deaths of women, striking about one out of every 10 American women. The American Cancer Society estimates that 143,000 new cases will occur this year, and predicts 43,000 deaths. 9/89

Poor Vision and Hip Fracture

Because vision deteriorates with age, the risk of hip

fractures from repeated falls increases — particularly among those 75 and over. Since a hip fracture often requires hospitalization and immobilization, it can be devastating.

Seniors can take steps so they are less vulnerable, say officials at Fair Oaks Hospital in Fairfax, Va. Those living alone can make changes in their homes to compensate for visual loss, such as removing geometrically patterned rugs that may cause illusions and contribute to a fall.

Hand rails should be installed in areas of the home where it is difficult to navigate, such as bathrooms and stairways. Also, obstacles below eye level, such as small tables and chairs, should be removed.

Of course, early detection and treatment of eye disease are important. Seniors should visit an eye specialist at least once a year (more frequently to ensure that current prescriptions are accurate). Seniors should also visit a specialist regularly so symptoms do not go undetected and untreated.
5/91

Make Every Voice Count

By Permission of Mell Lazarus and Creators Syndicate

GETTING PERSONAL

In this section, you'll meet some of the people who make the National Committee possible: Some of its staffers, and just a few of its millions of members and supporters.

• • •

National Committee Staff

It's hard to get National Committee staffers to sit still long enough to be profiled. Mostly, you've got to catch them running through the halls, around Washington, or around the country working to educate seniors about the issues and helping fight for their rights.

Martha McSteen, President

Mrs. McSteen has 39 years of experience with the Social Security Administration at every level, from claims representative to chief executive. She knows the system inside and out.

Mrs. McSteen joined the National Committee as senior legislative counsel in 1986, following her retirement from the Social Security Administration. She was named to the board of directors in 1988.

"The National Committee's dramatic growth over its first six years of existence has presented us with both challenges and opportunities," said Ms. McSteen in 1989 as she accepted her new duties as National Committee president.

"The challenge is to provide the kind of service National Committee members have a right to expect," she said. "The opportunity is for us to be even more effective in providing seniors with a strong, professional voice here in Washington.

"I feel strongly we can both meet our challenges and make use of our opportunities," Mrs. McSteen said. "That is my goal."

After serving 11 years as Regional Medicare Administrator in Denver and Dallas, Mrs. McSteen was named Regional Social Security Commissioner for Texas, Louisiana, Oklahoma, New Mexico and Arkansas. In 1983, she was tapped by the Reagan Administration to serve as acting commissioner, a post she held for three years.

During her career, she was twice cited as one of the nation's top civil service executives. In 1980, President Carter selected her for a Presidential Meritorious Executive Award. This was followed by President Reagan naming her a Presidential Distinguished Executive.

Lloyd Duxbury

Nearly 40 years of wisdom and expertise make National Committee Director of Legislation Lloyd Duxbury a valuable asset.

Duxbury, whose experience, savvy and humor make him one of the best liked staffers at the National Committee, is a tireless advocate for seniors' rights.

A native of Caledonia, Minn., Duxbury is a graduate of Harvard and Harvard Law School. After spending three years in the army during World War II — "I was the last man in the rear rank of the infantry division," he jokes — he began his legal career in a small firm founded by his grandfather.

In 1950, Duxbury ran for a seat in the Minnesota House of Representatives, fully intending to serve only one term if he won. He ended up serving for nearly 20 years. "I guess I sort of got to liking it," he explains.

Duxbury became minority leader of the Minnesota House in 1959 and again in 1961, and was House Speaker during four sessions beginning in 1963.

After stepping away from the public service limelight, he came to Washington, D.C., as the vice president Eastern Counsel for the Great Northern Railroad. He spent 12 years handling Congressional relations for the company.

At the end of 1981, Duxbury "involuntarily accepted voluntary early retirement," but he was not inactive for long. In 1982, with the help of some colleagues, he formed a non-profit organization to represent the interests of railroad retirees and, as its lobbyist, testified before several House and Senate Committees.

"Somebody once told me lobbying is the best job for a frustrated statesman," remarked Duxbury.

Duxbury met National Committee Executive Vice President Max Richtman in 1987 while both were with the Senate Special Aging Committee staff. He followed Richtman to the National Committee in April 1989, becoming a government relations representative. "Dux is a first rate attorney and brings a tremendous amount of legislative experience," said Richtman. "He was a key force in the repeal of the catastrophic [care] surtax and continues to be a major player in other legislative action."

At 69, Duxbury shows no sign of slowing down. "I really enjoy working with the National Committee," he said. "The issues are challenging and interesting, and I thrive on being around Capitol Hill. Besides, the people here are among the nicest I've met."

Martha Mohler

Work. Work. Work. Most people complain they don't have enough leisure time, but National Committee Health

Make Every Voice Count

Policy Analyst Martha Mohler is one of those people who thrives on work. Hers is a special goal: Nursing home improvement.

As a daughter of a nursing home resident, and later as the director of nursing at a suburban Maryland nursing home, Mrs. Mohler saw first hand the problems plaguing nursing homes — especially the shortage of quality, trained, dedicated nurses and nurse aides.

"The quality of care is directly proportional to nurses' competence and level of commitment, as long as there are enough people to do the work," says Mrs. Mohler. Inadequate budgets for nursing services and low salaries create a shortage of skilled nurses and high turnover.

Convinced changes in nursing home administration and public policy were needed to solve the problems, she went back to school, earning a master's degree in health services administration from George Washington University. While there, she interned from 1986-87 for the Senate Special Committee on Aging, then headed by the late Sen. John Heinz, R-Pa.

During her time with the Aging Committee, Mrs. Mohler worked on a study of nursing home staffing in conjunction with Congressional work on the 1987 Nursing Home Reform Act.

Mrs. Mohler continues her work to improve nursing home care at the National Committee. She and Research and Policy Development Manager William Lessard coauthored a study on nurse staffing issues which updates her work at the Aging Committee. New information confirms nursing homes still aren't adequately staffed and points out the need for more federal and state money to correct the problem.

"She believes passionately in improving care for the nursing home resident," says Lessard. "Someone with Martha's hands-on experience as a director of nursing in a nursing home is invaluable. She knows what it takes to provide quality care."

The study has been presented to several senior organizations in an effort to spark enthusiasm and emphasize the need for further nursing home reform.

"Martha's expertise in health care issues and sensitivity to the needs of nursing home residents is extraordinary," says National Committee President Martha McSteen. "She is a great asset to the National Committee and I am always pleased when she represents the National Committee at various meetings and seminars."

Monette McKinnon

Senior Grassroots Coordinator Monette McKinnon travels across the country, educating National Committee members, activists and community groups about important issues, events and legislation affecting seniors.

Ms. McKinnon also works with area agencies on aging and senior service provider groups to promote joint efforts on issues which concern National Committee members and other seniors.

"I feel very strongly about what the National Committee does, and I'm here because I like to help people," says Ms. McKinnon. "Before I came here five years ago, I wasn't as conscious about some of the pressing issues facing seniors today — working here certainly has been a real eye-opener."

Born in Vicksburg, Miss., Ms. McKinnon lived in Tennessee, New York and California before moving to northern Virginia 16 years ago.

After a stint with the American Psychiatric Association, she began her grassroots work with the Isaac Walton League, a conservation organization based in Washington, D.C.

Serving as liaison between the group's leadership

committees and coordinator of the group's resolution process, she also worked extensively with grassroots on various environmental litigation.

"My interest in grassroots work and aging issues has its evolution in the time I spent with the Isaac Walton League," she says.

"Monette's dedication to the members of the National Committee is unequaled," says National Committee President Martha McSteen. "She's enthusiastic, tireless and extremely bright. She's truly a grassroots person."

Since much of her time with the National Committee is spent traveling — "I can't remember a recent week when I wasn't on an airplane," she remarks — her free time is devoted to her son Chris, 14, an aspiring Shakespearean actor and "an all-around fantastic guy."

Ms. McKinnon is also a talented artist and quilter — most of her finished work goes to friends and family. She also enjoys reading historical novels, especially on medieval England and early English royalty.

Bente Cooney

Senior Policy Analyst Bente Cooney brings a touch of Denmark to the National Committee, and in doing so, hopes to change the face of health care in America.

Born and raised in Copenhagen, Ms. Cooney took the free health care of her native country for granted. She was able to spend a year at a nursing home/farm where her mother was a licensed practical nurse.

"My roots are very important to me," says Ms. Cooney. "They influence the way I think about health care, and the way I approach my job at the National Committee."

Mrs. Cooney came to the National Committee after several years with the House Select Committee on Aging. "I saw the National Committee as a strong advocate for seniors," she says. "I felt I could contribute to the formation of a significant long-term care policy for this nation."

Though she feels strongly about all issues affecting seniors, affordable health and long-term care are her top priorities. "A desperate need exists to streamline the health care system, especially Medicare, which can be extremely confusing to seniors," she says. "An unexpected illness can easily deplete a senior's life savings."

"Aging is difficult enough without fearing impoverishment should you need long-term care," Ms. Cooney remarks. "The present system is unfair and wrong, and I hope to help change it."

Along with her work with the National Committee, Ms. Cooney is co-chair of the National Capitol Chapter of the Older Women's League, and is the founder of Washingtonians for Improvement of Nursing Home (WINH) and Long Term Care.

"Bente is truly an advocate for long-term home health care and nursing home care. She is knowledgeable, dedicated and very persuasive in her arguments," said National Committee President Martha McSteen. "Members can count on her representing them well in Washington. She is a great asset to the National Committee."

As if this hectic schedule wasn't enough, Ms. Cooney is learning how to fly, and hopes to get her pilot's license this year.

"I love my job at the National Committee," she explains. "This is a good group of dedicated people."

Make Every Voice Count

Reprinted By Permission of North America Syndicate, Inc.

"Dr. Figby will now give us the benefit of his year of experience."

Meet the Members

National Committee members are the foundation of a powerful grassroots lobbying and education organization. President Martha McSteen and the National Committee staff appreciate the support and active involvement of all their members. They're all interesting people with a fascinating story to tell.

Edward Thomason

Family, home, hard work and community values are important to Edward Thomason.

Thomason has spent almost all his 74 years in or near Dawson Springs, Ky., a small town about 100 miles north of Nashville, Tenn. He was born there, raised there, and there met and wed his childhood sweetheart, Mary Louise Clark.

Dawson Springs is still home to the Thomasons. "It would be hard to leave such a beautiful, peaceful place," he says of the town, originally famous for its mineral springs.

Thomason's work also has kept him close to his beloved hometown. His furthest commute was to Evansville, Ind., where he worked at Republic Aviation building bodies for P47 Thunderbolts — fighter planes that played a key role in World War II.

After the war, Thomason worked as a service manager at two auto dealerships. But the desire to be his own boss led him to purchase a service station, which he owned and ran for 20 years.

"I always had a desire to be better than the average worker," says Thomason. "Plus you can make more money working for yourself."

The small town atmosphere of Dawson Springs even influenced the way Thomason conducted business. Most of the service station's first customers were coal miners who were extended credit on their word only, a common practice in rural areas. The unwritten repayment date was always payday, says Thomason.

Although Thomason enjoyed his work, he gladly retired early in 1984 at age 64 so he could spend more time with his family.

Upon retiring, Thomason became aware he was affected by the Notch inequity when he read an Ann Landers column in the newspaper. Deciding to do something about it, he took out an ad in the local newspaper offering information about the Notch. The ad generated more than 200 inquiries from Kentucky seniors who wanted to know what they could do to help correct the inequity.

He responded to each one with a letter explaining how the problem occurred and the status of legislation now in Congress. He also asked each correspondent to write his or her senators and representative, urging them to correct the Notch.

Thomason, a six-year member of the National Committee, commends the organization's efforts to correct the Notch as well as other problems affecting seniors.

"If other senior organizations were as involved as the National Committee, [Notch correction] legislation would already have been passed," he says.

Nan Rogers

A high school teacher in rural Kentucky unknowingly shaped the career of Nan Rogers.

Ms. Rogers admired that teacher and wanted to follow in her footsteps. When asked about colleges to attend, the teacher recommended her own alma mater, West Virginia State College, to study — what else? — education.

Mrs. Rogers' first teaching job was at an Alabama elementary school. It was there she met and wed her husband, Clarence.

About two year later, the couple moved to Connecticut, where Mrs. Rogers held a number of teaching and counseling positions. The last 17 years of her career were spent as a counselor at South Central Community College in New Haven. She truly enjoyed her job because of her interaction with the "wide diversity of races and religions of the student population," she says.

Mrs. Rogers is proud of her accomplishments and equally proud of her husband's. He was an admired and respected school administrator in New Haven but was forced to retire early because of a disabling illness. The community dedicated a newly built school in his honor several years before his death.

Mrs. Rogers wonders what life would have been like had she and her husband followed up on their one-time plan of opening a catering company. They decided against it because time with the family was too important, she says.

By age 60 she was "getting tired" of working, so Mrs. Rogers took early retirement. Instead of slowing down in her later years, Mrs. Rogers volunteers in community services which keep her more active than a full-time job.

She serves on the advisory boards of several senior organizations and is president of two groups whose goal is to correct problems affecting the black community, such as AIDS, teenage pregnancy, poverty and unemployment. In June, the New Haven YWCA recognized Mrs. Rogers' volunteer work.

She applauds the National Committee's work on issues affecting older women. "The National Committee and all its literature are great ways for seniors to learn about things which can impact their lives," says Mrs. Rogers.

James W. Latimer, Jr.

James W. Latimer, Jr. can't read music, but he's been playing in a band since the 1940s.

His music career started at age eight, when he made so much noise with his drums that his mother had to chase him into the garage, he says. During the 1940s, '50s and '60s, Latimer played the cymbals in parades and other festivities in which the Metropolitan Washington, D.C., Police Department participated

Latimer recently retired from the police department after serving as a desk sergeant. Since he worked a desk job, he had face-to-face contact with many of the "locals" who would come into the precinct for advice, to get out of the cold weather and sometimes just to pass the time.

Latimer began his police career as a beat policeman and patrolled the streets for about seven years. "I hated giving out parking tickets," he says. Sometimes he would wait to see if the person would return to his car before writing the ticket.

Latimer now enjoys retirement at his Marlow Heights, Md., home. Like most seniors, he is proud of his 67 years of age, and he hasn't let it slow him down. He helps other seniors in his community by driving them to medical appointments and the grocery store, and sometimes just acting as a companion.

After retiring, Latimer also joined an all-senior jazz band as a drummer. Being a senior is not a requirement to join the Happy Timers Band. It's just easier to find seniors since they're always at home, Latimer says.

Most of their performances are for local nursing home residents.

The group's leader and keyboard player, Evelyn Hudson, also is a National Committee member. In fact, she encouraged Latimer to join about three years ago. She and Latimer often discuss issues on which the National Committee is lobbying, such as the Notch and national health care. They agree the country needs a national health plan, especially because of the high cost of prescription drugs for seniors.

Any senior not currently a National Committee member should consider joining, says Latimer. "Most senior citizens don't realize there is strength in numbers. Everyone would have a stronger voice."

Raymond and Ann Kolb

Raymond and Ann Kolb of Clinton, Miss., spent more than 40 years in central Brazil as Southern Baptist missionaries, teaching theology and running schools.

Mr. Kolb also had a special duty while in Brazil. He piloted the mission's aircraft, ferrying supplies and guests to the school, and on evangelist weekend trips. The plane also served as a flying ambulance. Hospitals were more than 100 miles away during their early days in Brazil, so when someone needed immediate medical attention, he was always ready to fly.

Brazil was a second home to the senior Kolbs, but to

their children it was very much home. Two of their four children — two boys and two girls — were born in Brazil.

"We truly enjoyed our work.... We have wonderful friends in that part of the world," said Mrs. Kolb. Their family and Brazilian families were always welcome in each other's homes, she said. "Our children grew up with their children."

When asked about women's roles in Brazil, Mr. Kolb laughingly said women were "kept in their place" when the couple first arrived in the '40s. "Now it's a lot nearer to the United States' view of women."

She recalled the time someone gave the couple a car shortly after their arrival in the South American country. The first time she drove it into town, everyone stared at her — no one could believe a woman was actually driving, she said.

Today the Kolbs enjoy babysitting their grandchildren — seven altogether — and singing in the church choir. Mrs. Kolb said she has always loved music and was involved with it during their Brazil years, especially with schoolage children. Mr. Kolb continues to be active with his alma mater — Mississippi College — and speaks to church groups about mission work.

The Kolbs have been members of the National Committee for about two years. They believe the National Committee's first priority should be to "protect Social Security for the future — not just for us, but for our children and grandchildren."

Likewise, Mrs. Kolb said, Medicare should be preserved because, "it helps a lot of people. We have been very happy with Medicare and Social Security and how they have helped us." However, the system should be checked regularly to avoid abuse, they say.

Leonard Fortner

National Committee member Leonard Fortner is dedicated to correcting the Notch inequity and to polishing the tarnished image of the insurance industry in which he has worked nearly 40 years.

"People are always portraying the insurance industry as the bad guy, trying to coerce unsuspecting seniors into buying unnecessary policies," says Fortner. "I don't want it to earn a bad name for the actions of a few unscrupulous salesmen."

Born in Kannapolis, N.C., in 1923, Fortner is a Notch victim — "I'm fighting with you on this one," he says — and writes often to lawmakers urging them to join other supporters to correct the Notch.

During World War II, Fortner served with Gen. Omar Bradley's headquarters in Europe. He was a private in a special platoon whose job it was to see that Bradley's offices got what they needed when they needed it. He also made sure actors and singers coming to entertain troops in Europe were well taken care of.

After the war, Fortner remained in Europe to serve officers and attorneys in route to the trials at Nuremburg. "We made sure they were comfortable and had adequate quarters," he says. "This was one of the most interesting aspects of my European tour of duty."

After his return to the U.S., he began his long career in the insurance industry. Starting as a sales agent, he was assigned to Martinsville, Va., and then to Johnson City, Tenn., where he and his family have remained since.

"Johnson City is beautiful, surrounded by mountains — I wouldn't live anywhere else," he says.

Though he took early retirement from his company, Fortner continues to work full-time for his own agency. "It is still a lot of fun, especially with the people in this area," he says. He also has qualified as a member of the Million Dollar Round Table, a professional organization exemplifying excellence in production and service in the insurance industry.

Fortner has been married for nearly 50 years to Mary Lee. The couple has five children. He enjoys golfing — he has a 12 handicap — and is a dedicated University of Tennessee supporter.

As a National Committee member, Fortner has taken advantage of the services the organization has to offer. "The National Committee appreciates what I have to say," remarks Fortner. "Their staff always goes the extra mile, and I appreciate that."

Your Voice Helps Strengthen Social Security and Medicare

Dear Reader:

The National Committee draws its strength from individuals like you who support and want to improve the U.S. Social Security and Medicare systems.

I hope that reading this book will help you understand the issues facing seniors today and what the National Committee is doing about them.

The National Committee is widely recognized as a leading national group fostering Social Security and Medicare, one of the most effective grassroots advocacy organizations in U.S. history.

The National Committee keeps members and friends abreast of the impact of current issues and proposals affecting the future of all U.S. seniors by publications such as our *Saving Social Security* newspaper and our "Senior Flash" telephone hotline.

Also, the National Committee amplifies the voices of millions of members and supporters, and makes their wishes known and respected in the halls of Congress, in the White House, in the federal bureaucracy, and in all other areas where senior rights may be threatened.

I thank you for your support if you already are a National Committee member. And, if you have not joined yet, I urge you to do so now!

Sincerely,

Martha A. McSteen
President
National Committee to Preserve
Social Security and Medicare